COLUMBIA COLLEGE
621.47H157F   C1   V 0
FABULOUS FIREBALL$ NEW YORK

3 2711 00003 8599

YO-CUL-652

LIBRARY
OF
COLUMBIA COLLEGE
CHICAGO, ILLINOIS

JAN '98

Fabulous
Fireball

Also by D. S. Halacy, Jr.

STAR FOR A COMPASS

HIGH CHALLENGE

BY D. S. HALACY, JR.

FABULOUS FIREBALL

The Story of Solar Energy

Illustrated with photographs

**THE
MACMILLAN COMPANY**
New York, 1961

© THE MACMILLAN COMPANY 1957

All rights reserved—no part of this book may be reproduced in any form without permission in writing from the publisher, except by a reviewer who wishes to quote brief passages in connection with a review written for inclusion in magazine or newspaper.

Library of Congress catalog card number: 57-10014

Jacket photograph by Earl S. Ream

Third Printing, 1961

PRINTED IN THE UNITED STATES OF AMERICA

For My Daughter, Jessie Ann

Contents

INTRODUCTION		ix
ONE	Meet the Sun	1
TWO	Myth, Legend, and History	14
THREE	Solar Cookers	26
FOUR	Solar Furnaces	39
FIVE	Solar Air Conditioning	54
SIX	Something New Under the Sun!	68
SEVEN	Food and Water from the Sun	81
EIGHT	Power from the Sun	94
NINE	More Power from the Sun	107
TEN	The Solar Scientist	120
ELEVEN	Solar-Powered Space Ships	133
TWELVE	The Sun Tomorrow	143

INTRODUCTION

One hundred years ago, when steam engines and water wheels were the only means available for producing power, men in the United States and in many other nations sought ways to use the sun's energy. Less than fifty years ago, great solar engines were built in Arizona and California to pump water for irrigation. The largest of all solar machines was finished in Egypt just before World War I, to raise water from the River Nile.

When the steam turbine and the gasoline engine became available virtually everywhere, these solar engines were discarded and their inventors were all but forgotten. Only in those areas of the world where fuels were scarce did men continue to dream of ways to use the unending flow of energy from the sun. Meanwhile, the demand for conventional fuels—wood, coal, oil, and natural gas—increased rapidly. Today, more and more energy is needed for automobiles and airplanes, farms and factories, and to heat and cool our homes.

Once again, men are beginning to give serious thought to ways and means for using the sun's energy. We know that we are consuming our supply of fossil fuels with alarming rapidity, and even our newest energy source, atomic fission, depends upon a relatively limited supply of uranium and thorium. Solar radiation remains as the world's only inexhaustible source of energy, but before we reach the point where we can make use of this endless resource, many discoveries will have to be made. Energy storage methods, large area solar-electric cells, catalysts for photo-activated decomposition of water—these are some of the fields where new knowledge is needed.

These discoveries will in all probability be made by men and women who are today still boys and girls in school. The scientists of tomorrow who turn to the study of the sun will do so because their interest and curiosity have been aroused by books such as Mr. Halacy's FABULOUS FIREBALL. He gives a good background on the scientific aspects of solar energy, and his glimpse of what may come in the future is intriguing. The Association for Applied Solar Energy welcomes this addition to the growing body of information on the sun and the ways in which mankind will make use of it.

John I. Yellott,
Executive Director
Association for Applied Solar Energy

May, 1957

CHAPTER
ONE

Meet the Sun

In a very real sense, we were born of the sun. Ages ago our earth was wrenched from its parent and hurled a tremendous distance away. Today, we still look to the sun for nurture; we live in the sun or die, as one writer has said. The sun has given everything, including a name, to our solar system.

The sun holds us in an orbit, keeping us from flying off into outer space and disaster. It warms us, and grows our crops. We see by its light, and it causes our weather. Sailing ships, windmills, and waterfalls all owe their existence to the sun. Sunbathers and navigators alike depend on the sun, though for very different reasons.

Quite recently in our history, men worshiped the sun, and an eclipse was enough to terrify superstitious natives who feared that such a thing foretold the end of the world. Today, we no longer worship the sun but serious-minded scientists eye it with a new and growing respect.

When you turn on television, cook dinner, or drive the family car across town, stop and think where the power comes from. Electricity, natural gas, and petroleum of course; but all these fuels come from something much more basic. The source of power is that ball of fire up in the sky some ninety-three million miles away. Quite literally the sun makes the world go 'round!

Every ounce of energy in wood, coal, oil and gas was put there over a long period of time by the sun shining on the earth and storing up heat. In fact, we refer to these as "fossil fuels" to indicate how long it took to create them. When we burn fossil fuels we simply release stored energy, much like running water from a tank.

Once men thought these fuels would last forever. Forests were stripped and no one was too concerned, for coal and petroleum deposits were being found faster than they could be used. Now, however, the picture has changed completely. Experts believe that our known reserves of all types of fuel, including the atomic materials, will last only a few hundred years *at present rates of consumption*.

These scientists know too that man is using power in greatly increasing amounts each year, so present consumption is not a realistic method of computing the time we have left. For example, jet airplanes gulp fuel much faster than the old types did—one new fighter plane has a horsepower rating of 60,000! And guided missiles and rockets consume fuel in a way to make conservationists fearful.

Our automobiles now use more fuel as engines grow larger; even closer to home are the other demands we make. Comfortably heated and cooled houses have become necessities today, and power-consuming appliances continue to grow in popularity. All over the world, but

Association For Applied Solar Energy

SCOUTS LEARNING basic facts about solar energy. Much of it is reflected or absorbed by the atmosphere. Rain, and the rest of our weather, depends on the sun.

particularly in America, people have become "power-mad" in a different meaning of the term.

Modern technology is taxing our dwindling fuel supplies. As it becomes increasingly necessary to use low-grade ores, for example, more power is required to process metal. Our chemical industry cuts into petroleum and coal reserves, with detergents and synthetic fibres taking the place of "natural" materials. Then too, work animals are being replaced with power equipment. This further depletes the fossil fuel reserve.

There is another big reason why the bottom of the fuel barrel is nearly in sight. Population is increasing tremendously and is expected to *triple* in the next century. What this will do to the stockpile is as alarming as it is unavoidable. A hundred and fifty years ago an Englishman named Malthus warned that existing methods could not feed and support much increase in population. Improved methods and industrialization met the challenge then, but we are now faced with a grimmer prospect.

In Malthus' day, only the surface of the world's fuel supply had been scratched. Today prospectors are scrambling to find new supplies. Even if the optimists are right and huge new supplies of fossil fuels are discovered along with more atomic materials, the result will be only a delaying of the inevitable result. This is because of one inescapable fact: *Fossil fuels and atomic materials, once used, are gone forever!* Man cannot wait the ages necessary for nature to again build him an easy-to-use stockpile of what scientists call "chocolate-bar" fuels.

The use of simple woodburning engines has been suggested as a possible power supply. Trees grow rapidly, and fairly efficient engines might be made. However it is obvious that enough wood cannot be grown to supply the whole world even if the transportation problem could be solved. Taking all factors into consideration, responsible men predict that we will begin to feel the pinch of power shortage as early as 1975.

This is the prime reason for interest in solar energy, for if man cannot wait for stored, secondhand power, he must use it directly from the sun. For an idea of the tremendous possibilities, consider this: *Every three days, the sun showers the earth with the equivalent energy of all the stored fuel reserves known!* To better understand this amazing fact, let's take a good look at Sol.

Our sun is actually an orange dwarf "star." Although it is not nearly the hottest star known, its surface has a temperature of about 10,000 degrees F. and its interior is thought to be in the range of twenty *million* degrees. We commonly think of the sun as burning, yet it is too hot to burn and is composed of elemental gases. On the surface this gas is thin and tenuous, but so great is the gravity of the sun that at its center it has a density six times that of the element, mercury.

The sun is 864,000 miles in diameter, and has a mass one third of a million times greater than earth. Scientists believe it is two billion years old, and that instead of cooling, it is still getting hotter. Perhaps in another two billion years it will have reached a temperature sufficient to destroy the earth. Long after that, the sun will wane and gradually cool.

For centuries men have pondered the source of the fantastic quantities of heat and light the sun beams into space. Now it is thought that the fusion of hydrogen atoms results in the formation of helium, with heat energy as a by-product. Helium, the gas used in dirigibles and balloons, was first discovered in the sun and takes its name from the Greek word for sun.

The sun's corona, or halo, is almost as hot as its interior. Solar prominences—tongues of hot gas—leap outward from the surface a half-million miles at speeds reaching 250,000 miles an hour. Fortunately these prominences do not reach the ninety-three million miles to earth, nor are the terrific temperatures transmitted through space. Some of the energy from these disturbances does reach our atmosphere however, and is believed to cause changes in weather.

Using an instrument called a coronagraph, scientists observe the east "limb" of the sun. Since the sun rotates once in twenty-eight days, the sector observed moves to face the earth in a week and makes it possible to predict general weather changes that far ahead.

Besides weather, solar activity affects radio reception too. The Aurora Borealis, or northern lights, are caused by the glowing of gases high in our atmosphere when they are struck by energy particles from the sun. These things are provable, and Dr. C. G. Abbot, dean of solar scientists, feels that the sun's influence is much more basic than is generally realized. He compares its cycles to those of human life. Other researchers claim to show a correlation between wars in past centuries and sunspot activity! Perhaps in time these things will be proved; for the present it is interesting enough to know that the sun is constantly bombarding us with "bullets" of heat energy that we can put to work.

The saying that there is nothing new under the sun has

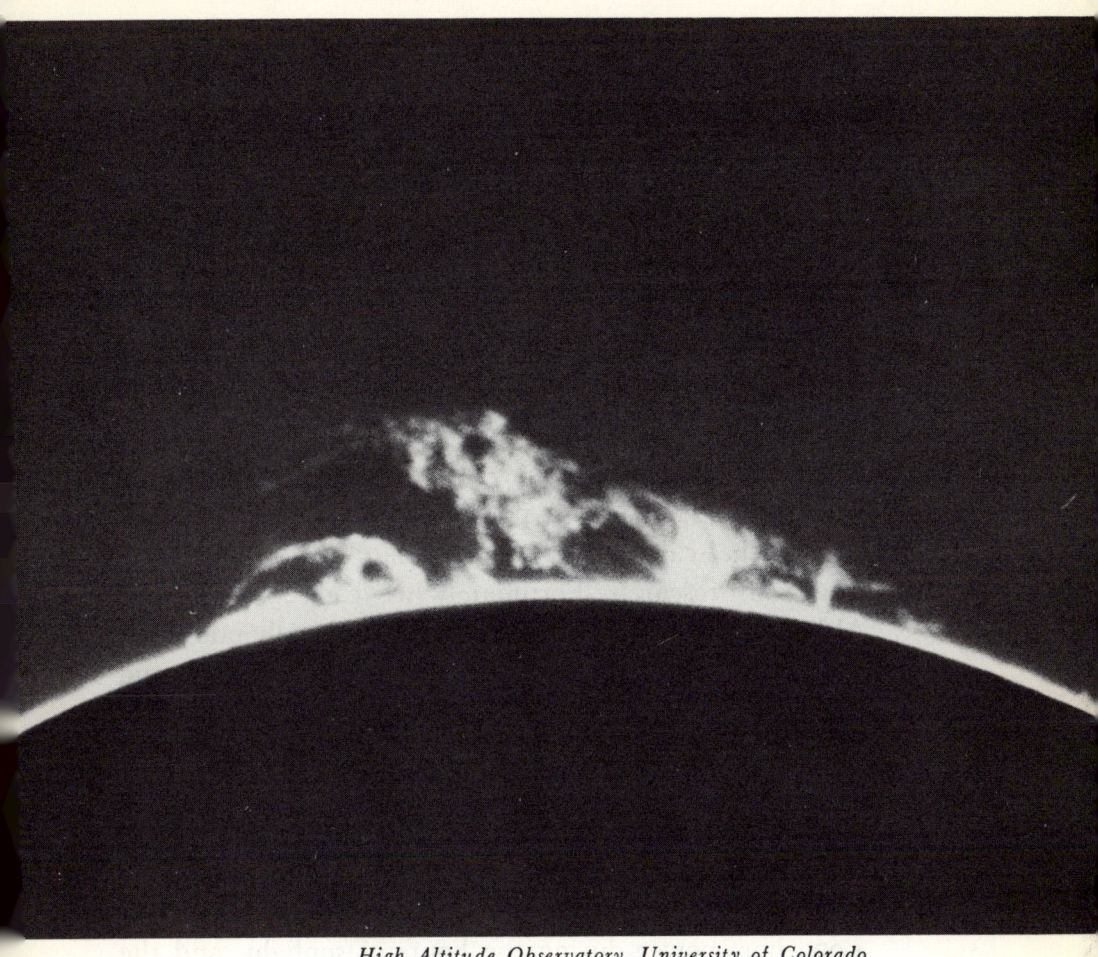

High Altitude Observatory, University of Colorado

SOLAR PROMINENCES leaping from the surface of the sun. These tongues of hot gas extend thousands of miles outward. This photograph was taken with the coronagraph of the High Altitude Observatory of the University of Colorado.

some truth in it. A hundred years ago men built steam engines using solar heat, and Samuel Pierpont Langley, whose flying machine vied with the Wrights', built a solar oven which he took to the top of Mt. Whitney to cook a meal.

Despite these and other experiments, interest in solar energy lagged. Other forms of power were simpler to use, so man used them. Wood was burned, then coal, oil and gas. Finally electricity was made from other fuels, and with seemingly endless reserves there was no pressure to do otherwise.

Now it appears that our wastefulness has caught up with us. The hunger for power and the sobering knowledge of the scant supply of "chocolate bar" fuel is spurring solar research. Fortunately we can be optimistic. Although the energy reaching the earth is only one thousand millionth of the sun's total, it is still two thousand times the requirements of even those of us in America. We are the biggest power-users in the world, and yet it has been estimated that the roof of the average house receives and wastes many times more energy than comes in through electric wires!

One acre of ground in the southern United States gets 4,000 horsepower during the hours of sunlight, and the solar energy falling on Lake Mead is five times greater than power generated in the Boulder Dam hydroelectric plant. This sun energy is "diffuse," or at a low concentration, and will challenge the ingenuity of the "heliotechnologist" to use it efficiently. But use it we must, or someday do without.

A different kind of hunger in some parts of the world gives impetus to solar research. In lands where food and

Association For Applied Solar Energy

OUTDOOR EXHIBITS at the First World Solar Symposium held in Phoenix, Arizona, November 1955. The theme was "The Sun At Work," and solar devices of all kinds from all over the world were displayed.

fuel are scarce, solar energy may be used for cooking and thus save valuable fertilizers now being burned. UNESCO and other agencies are promoting the use of simple solar stoves in lands where there is an abundance of sunshine.

Along with hunger there is thirst. Underground water, stored over long ages of time, is being depleted rapidly and wells are drying up. Sea water, made drinkable by solar distillation, is a possible solution to this problem.

One solar scientist has made the statement that while man does not live by kilowatts alone there is much hope for the prosperity of the world in the use of solar energy. This is particularly true in depressed areas. Israel is an example, and Jerusalem's recent exposition, "Conquest of the Desert" was a glimpse of how the wasteland may someday blossom. India has produced thousands of solar stoves, and in Japan algae is cultivated with solar heat to be used as a food supplement.

Obviously it is not as simple to use solar energy as it is to burn a log. John Ericsson, famous as the builder of the *Monitor* in the Civil War, spent twenty years experimenting with solar engines. In the end he sadly stated that such power was ten times as costly as other methods.

Ericsson and the others did not have the benefit of recent advances in allied sciences, and today the picture is far brighter. Researchers in more than thirty countries are busy, and they profit from the help of an organization called The Association For Applied Solar Energy. Formed in 1954, this group held the first World Symposium on solar energy, in Arizona. The theme of the affair was "The Sun At Work," and the many displays lived up to that title.

Solar furnaces melted high-temperature materials like

Association For Applied Solar Energy

THE LARGEST SOLAR furnace in the world. This curved mirror, designed by Dr. Felix Trombe, was built in an old fort in the Pyrenees Mountains of southern France. Generating nearly 3,300 degrees C., it is used in research and also to melt tons of metal and other material for industry. The reflector, composed of 3,500 small mirrors, is 35 feet across.

platinum, and solar engines pumped water for irrigation purposes. The sun powered radios, telephones and clocks. It generated steam and fired jewelry kilns, besides cooking meals. The Symposium was the merest hint of what is being done, right now, in the field of solar energy.

In France's Pyrenees mountains, a huge solar furnace, thirty-five feet across, melts hundred-pound chunks of iron to produce the purest alloys known. Russia has a furnace of about the same size, and also a solar machine that produces 600 pounds of ice a day! Algeria has a large furnace which can make fertilizer by fixation of nitrogen in the atmosphere.

Homes have long been heated by the sun, but now scientists are beginning to refrigerate them as well. Solar "batteries" have powered telephone lines and can store energy for nighttime requirements. One scientist foresees solar collectors installed along the right-of-way on railroad lines to provide electricity for driving the train. And promising work has been done in the breakdown of water into hydrogen and oxygen, simply by exposure to sunlight. The gases thus obtained are excellent fuels.

Truly, the sun has been put to work, even though the harness is a light one as yet. Each day Sol rises patiently, to shower us with far more power than we need, if we can only learn how to use it efficiently. The task won't be easy, but it must be done. Our scientists know this, and so do the men of industry. Our schools know it too, and quite probably we will some day have men trained especially as solar scientists—"heliotechnologists."

These things are fact, not science-fiction. With each chapter of this book, we will explore a particular phase of solar energy. We will discuss the possibilities and the difficulties, for there are many of both. All over the world, intelligent men are looking to the sun. The same rays strike American and Japanese, Russian and Frenchman. The same sun that cooks a meal for an Egyptian camel driver will produce electricity in a solar battery in Australia.

At present the atom seems geared to the task of destruction, while the sun offers power suited for peaceful tasks. If there is one international possession that can help tie us together, it is the sun. In the years to come, that will be increasingly important to us all.

CHAPTER TWO

Myth, Legend, and History

Since the sun is the center of our solar system, and such a spectacular one at that, it is easy to understand why man has attributed supernatural power to the sun. From the time he began to think, he turned to the flaming ball of fire in the heavens to explain the unexplainable.

Ra, the early Egyptian Sun-god, was probably derived from an even earlier West Asian deity. The cult of Ra was all-powerful for a long time, and at Heliopolis, the sun capital, there was a sacred tree of Ra, and even a pool where he bathed each evening! Ra had created himself from Nun, the void, and when he tired of ruling Egypt, he ascended to heaven on the back of a celestial sacred cow. He remains there to this day.

Mythology of every land treated the sun as supreme. Apollo was the Sun-god of both the Greeks and Romans. When his son, Phaethon, tried to drive the fiery chariot across the sky, he came too near the earth and catastrophe resulted.

Medea and Circe were thought to be daughters of the

sun, and the sun was the basis for the Golden Fleece Jason sought. In Norse mythology Balder's death in midwinter represents the annual "death" of the sun. Even in the comparatively recent Old Testament, Joshua was buried in the Sun-Palace. Job was told to look at the Sun "when he shined," and *Beth-shemesh* means House of Sun.

The sun was the deity of the Incas. Huge temples were erected in its name at the capital of Cuzco. The Sun-god was symbolized by great discs of gold, and this design was continued in later years by Mexican sun-worshippers. Natives of Brazil thought of the sun as a great spirit who could assume human shape at will.

Our own North American Indians, including the Natchez, Crow, Pueblo, Apache, Navajo, Papago, Cherokee, Iroquois, Blackfoot and Sioux regarded the sun as a chief deity. A legend of the Yuchi tells this charming story of the spirit, On-coye-to.

In the beginning there was no land, only vast dark regions of water. On-coye-to hovered above the water until exhausted, and then dropped like a white feather to its surface. As he did, a whirlwind spun him about on the waves so rapidly that the foam became land for On-coye-to to rest upon.

On-coye-to, though safe, still had no light, until wistfully he saw a distant star, called "Po-ko-lil-ey." He resolved then to bring light to the earth. Visiting the star he found it inhabited by a race of beautiful people. On-coye-to was welcomed everywhere except into the "sweathouse" which was the secret of the wonderful light.

The sweathouse could be visited only by the sick, since the light had magical curative powers. On the day of a big hunt, On-coye-to pretended to be ill and was permitted

—15—

to enter the sweathouse. Inside were many baskets, each holding a small, bright sun. On-coye-to stole one of the baskets and fled back to earth, hotly pursued by the star-dwellers.

Reaching his own land safely, he hung the sun in its basket up in the sky to light all the earth. Unfortunately the light was not quite right, and On-coye-to has been trying it in different parts of the sky ever since!

Another age-old theme is the "sun-snarer." A young Indian brave lay down to sleep in the noon sun, and his new jacket was shrunk by its heat. Angry, he fashioned a noose and fastened the sun in the sky. The earth soon grew unbearably hot, and in panic all the animals attempted to gnaw the bonds and free the sun. At last the mouse, then the biggest of the animals, succeeded. The sun moved again, but the mouse was reduced to his present tiny size from the heat he suffered.

Eskimo mythology tells of two young lovers who discovered to their sorrow that they were really brother and sister. The girl fled bitterly into the sky to become the sun, and the boy was changed into the moon. The Ojibwa tribe has a similar legend, and also celebrates the "white dog feast," since it is believed the sun and moon eat this meat in heaven.

A tale handed down in Polynesian folklore describes the sun as having once sped across the sky with terrific speed. A young native, angered because of the shortness of the day, solved the problem by simply breaking the sun's leg! With the sun proceeding across the heavens at a more leisurely rate, men could complete their tasks.

So deep-rooted are these myths and legends that they have persisted throughout long centuries. It is said that when Eskimo children play "cat's-cradle" or cup-and-ball, they speak even now of snaring the sun again. Indian sun-dances are still common, and lest we smile in a superior way, don't we call our religious day *Sun*day?

Along with devout worshippers of the sun there were also those who irreverently dreamed of putting the sun to work. These dreamers in time became inventors, and the burning glass was a result of their imagination. The Athenian, Aristophanes, was born in 448 B.C. and mentions the device in his writing. In his comedy, "The Clouds," a character explains how he gets the better of men to whom he owes money. The trick is simply to aim a burning glass at the wax tablet whereon the debt is recorded; a unique way of wiping out an obligation!

The old story of Daedalus and Icarus tells of one of the first aviators coming to grief because of the sun which melted his wax wings. Archimedes, however, turned the sun to his own advantage and used it to rout the enemy. Way back in 214 B.C. the man so famous for levers and other scientific principles was first to use solar energy as a weapon of war. When a Roman fleet attacked Syracuse, Archimedes used "a burning glass composed of small square mirrors, moving every way on hinges—so as to reduce the fleet to ashes at a distance of a bow shot!"

Apparently the Romans profited by the experience in an unusual way for in 77 A.D. Pliny wrote of the use of the burning glass to light fires and also in the field of medicine to burn away dead flesh. Later, in the siege of Constantinople, another Greek by the name of Proclus duplicated Archimedes' triumph by burning an enemy fleet. As usual, the Greeks had a word for it. Helios, an alternate to

Apollo, was their name for the sun. It is represented in our language by *heliograph*, *helium* and many other words.

After Proclus burned the enemy fleet, there was a long lapse in recorded solar history. Eclipses occasionally made the superstitious tremble in their boots, and it is not until 1615 that we find the first solar engine constructed. A man named de Caux was the inventor of this device that pumped water. The engine worked on the principle of air expanded by the sun's heat, and the amazing thing about it is that it was built a hundred and fifty years before Watt built his steam engine.

In 1695 two Italians, Averoni and Targioni, succeeded in "burning" a diamond, using a large magnifying lens. English and German lensmakers were making large glasses by this time and the French Duc d'Orleans used a German lens 33 inches in diameter in many experiments. Oddly, the solar furnace was used to "prove" the erroneous "phlogiston" theory of combustion and it was years before the mistake was rectified.

It remained for a French naturalist, Georges Buffon, to show once and for all that Archimedes' feat was not mere legend. Using a number of small mirrors, Buffon burned wood at a distance of 200 feet, which is about a "bow-shot." He also melted lead from 130 feet, and silver at a distance of half that much. Buffon, along with Cassini, was the first to curve mirrors into the parabolic shape used in today's solar furnaces.

Louis XIV was called "The Sun-King" and rightly so. During his reign much solar research was carried out. M. Antoine Lavoisier was the foremost solar scientist of

Association For Applied Solar Energy

FIRST MILITARY USE of solar energy! With a mirror arrangement of this type, Archimedes beat off an attacking Roman fleet by setting fire to ships' sails. This took place in the year 214 B.C., and the device ignited the sails "at the distance of a bow shot."

the next generation, and for a time it seemed France would continue to honor researchers. Lavoisier used the solar furnace first to disprove the false "phlogiston" theory. He showed that no substance was formed during combustion, but that the burning material simply combined with oxygen.

Next he built furnaces nearly twice the diameter of any earlier designs. These were curved glass sections, joined together and filled with wine! With them Lavoisier melted materials like platinum, achieving temperatures of nearly 2,000 degrees Centigrade. He also melted in a vacuum, and was first to observe that "the fire of ordinary furnaces seems less pure than that of the sun."

Then, abruptly, with the coming of the Revolution, Lavoisier became a martyr for science. Executioners beheaded him with the cry, "The Republic has no need for scientists!" It is a tribute to this early solar scientist that the factory at St. Gobain which made his lenses, today makes mirrors for the largest solar furnace in the world—in France. And a prime advantage cited by experts is that solar heat *is* "pure," as Lavoisier noted more than 150 years ago.

Men continued to dream of fantastic things. Cyrano de Bergerac in his "L'Histoire Comique des Etats et Empires du Soleil" describes a spaceship that journeys to the sun. It is powered by solar energy. Before we laugh too loudly at Cyrano, consider that two serious-minded scientists recently suggested spaceships powered by—solar energy!

We have mentioned the solar engine designed and built by de Caux, commenting that this was the first such device before Watt's steam engine. Another was produced

Association For Applied Solar Energy

HERE, IN MODEL FORM, is M. Lavoisier's lens-type solar furnace with which he melted platinum and other high-temperature materials and also disproved the erroneous theory that a substance called "phlogiston" was formed by the process of burning. Lavoisier was beheaded during the French Revolution because "the Republic has no need of scientists!"

in 1827, and by the latter half of that century solar engines began to appear steadily.

Mouchot built a solar pump and a water-distiller. John Ericsson, an American by adoption, designed a solar steam engine and several hot-air engines. Built in New York, the largest of these delivered one horsepower for each 100 feet of solar collector area.

Bombay, India, got its first solar steam engine in 1876, a power plant developing $2\frac{1}{2}$ horsepower. In 1880 for the first time solar energy literally made the news when a Frenchman operated his printing press with a solar engine!

At the turn of the century there was a flurry of solar activity in the western United States. A pioneer researcher built huge, cone-shaped reflectors in Pasadena, California, and in Tempe and Willcox, Arizona. These had a collecting area of 700 square feet and were used to pump water. A search is being made in Arizona to locate one built there, for it is believed stored away somewhere.

In 1901 the *Scientific American* described a "band of Boston capitalists" who built a solar engine on the Pasadena Ostrich Farm. Far from being men to hide their heads in the sand, this group produced a device developing 11 horsepower and capable of pumping 1400 gallons of water a minute. It was their hope "that such an engine would result in arid lands blooming as the rose." The one flaw in their plan was that they were years ahead of their time.

California, the land of sunshine always, saw another successful solar engine take shape at Needles in 1905. This developed 20 horsepower, but the builders admitted the cost of construction was about four times that of a conventional plant.

Association For Applied Solar Energy

JOHN ERICSSON'S "Caloric Engine," evidence of the genius of the man who built the famous *Monitor* during the Civil War. Constructed in 1883, this device concentrated the sun's rays with the curved reflector and used the hot air produced to operate an engine.

This same economic truth was learned by The Eastern Sun Power Company, Limited. This organization built the largest solar power plant ever; one with 100 horsepower capacity near Cairo, Egypt. While it operated successfully, it was abandoned during World War I because it could not compete with fuel-fired systems.

Early in this century Dr. C. G. Abbot produced solar power to broadcast a nationwide radio program. In New Mexico a solar pump lifted water into a large tank, which in turn released it to generate electricity which lighted a mine for many years. In Europe and Asia and elsewhere in the world solar heat has long evaporated the water in shallow pools to leave salt. This idea has been taken a step farther and used to purify salt or brackish water.

Eighty-five years ago a huge solar still, covering 51,000 square feet, was built in Las Salinas, Chile. With the sun as the only fuel, this device provided 5,000 gallons of pure water a day, distilled from the brackish supply on hand. Man had come a long way from the ignorant, quaking savage who sacrificed humans on the altar to the sun.

For centuries the sun has parched corn and dried meat for man to eat. In 1837, an inventor named Herschel found a way to step up the heat from the sun and was able to cook vegetables and stew meat in a wooden solar stove. Samuel Pierpont Langley, better known as the builder of what was nearly the first airplane to fly, constructed a solar oven too. In 1884 he lugged it to the top of Mt. Whitney and cooked a meal there.

Since the solar stove is perhaps the simplest application of sun heat, we shall begin our discussion of modern solar devices with it. In the next chapter we learn about different types of solar stoves.

Association For Applied Solar Energy

HERE, AT THE Solar Energy Symposium in 1955, a modern-day scientist duplicates Archimedes feat of using mirrors to start fire at a distance. Charred wood in the foreground is proof of the concentrating effect of mirrors focused on their target.

CHAPTER
THREE

Solar Cookers

Nearly everyone has used a magnifying lens for a burning glass, perhaps even to start a campfire for cooking. Some people have dried food in the sun, and this is a slow form of solar cookery. Even publicity-seekers who fry eggs on the scorching pavement in July are using a crude sun stove! But few of us have ever used an efficient, fast-acting reflector stove or oven, simply because we have so many other fuels available to us.

Fortunately wood is still plentiful in our country, and we can also use charcoal or liquid fuel in camp stoves. It is interesting, however, to consider the advantages of solar cooking. No matches are needed to light the sun stove and there is no flame to create a fire hazard. Carrying along, or gathering fuel on the spot, is not necessary. Solar heat is free, and without smoke, soot or ashes. Add to all this the thrill of cooking a meal with energy literally picked from the air, and you have the essence of solar cookery.

Recently a group of skiers climbed the mountains near Denver, Colorado, in mid-winter. Knee-deep in snow, they

Black Star

SKIERS COOKING lunch high in snowy mountains of Colorado. The solar stove called an "Umbroiler," was invented by Dr. George Löf. It is collapsible for easy carrying, and the silvered inner surface concentrates the sun's rays to produce heat for cooking.

set up a folding stove that looked suspiciously like an umbrella with its inner surface silvered and a small grill attached to the handle. Then, without matches, fuel, or flames, they cooked a meal for the party.

This ultra-modern solar stove is far removed from the earliest of sun cookers but based on the same principle used by pioneers more than a hundred years ago.

In the last chapter, the Herschel solar cooker was mentioned. Built in 1837, this mahogany box, fitted with a glass panel and buried in the sand, cooked vegetables and stewed meat for its inventor. Simple in principle and construction, it generated a temperature of 240 degrees and was called a "hotbox" type of cooker. We are all familiar with the greenhouse, the glass-surfaced structure which lets in the rays of the sun and traps them inside. Herschel's cooker functioned in this manner, heat coming through the glass but unable to escape through the one-way "valve" of the glass partition.

The main disadvantage to this first-recorded cooker was the fact that it could not be moved easily, and while it could have been easily buried at the beach, a picnic on hard ground would have posed a problem! Samuel Langley overcame this difficulty with his better insulated hotbox cooker in 1882. To prove how handy it was to take about, Langley carried it with him on a hiking trip to the top of Mt. Whitney in 1884 and cooked his meals.

Both these solar cookers used only the direct rays of the sun. The first model to use mirrors to concentrate solar heat was a more efficient design, an eight-sided, tapered box a little over two feet across at the large end. This cooked vegetables and meat for its inventor in Bombay, India, in 1876.

Association For Applied Solar Energy

SOLAR STOVES in action. These lightweight aluminum cookers were invented by Dr. Adnan Tarcici, delegate to the U. N. from Lebanon. Made in sections, the reflector can be folded and packed in a small case. To be operated, the stove is faced so that the sun's rays are reflected onto the bottom of the cooking pan. Temperature at the focal point is greater than 1,000 degrees!

Dr. Abbot, whom we have mentioned before, also built a solar stove using mirrors to concentrate heat. Thinking that cooking out-of-doors might not always be practical, he designed an oven with a remote heating unit. Besides being more convenient, this type was not subject to cooling by winds as is the case where the oven itself is placed in the sun.

Obviously, the one big difficulty with a solar stove is that the sun does not shine all day. Abbot realized this, and improved his oven to the point where it would store heat and cook twenty-four hours a day. To prove it could be done, he baked biscuits in a small oven at any hour.

But why should people consider solar stoves when other types were more convenient, and fuels readily available? Even in lands where fuel was becoming scarce, a phenomenon called *inertia* tended to keep natives doing as their fathers and grandfathers had done before them.

Today, however, the solar stove is coming to be thought of not merely as a clever gadget but a useful piece of equipment in places like India, Egypt, and Japan. Besides being short of fuel, India is lacking in food as well. Unfortunately, manure that might better fertilize the soil is used as fuel. UNESCO is much concerned with this, and has done work in the field of solar cooking.

One researcher has designed and built ovens which might be practical for depressed areas. Of metal, with hinged reflectors to focus the sun's rays inside, this oven also stores heat in cans of Glauber's salt, a material which can hold great quantities of heat. After sunset the salt releases this heat and continues to cook. Thus the evening meal may be prepared after dark.

This oven has been demonstrated countless times and

ALUMINUM SOLAR COOKER designed by M. L. Ghai for the National Physical Laboratory of India. This type stove is mass produced in factories in India, and sold for about fourteen dollars. The side of this cooker is cut on a straight line so that it may be used even in the early morning and late at night when the sun is very low in the sky.

has proved itself in the field. Compact, and generating up to 400 degrees of heat, it can be mass-produced for as little as five dollars. This should make it a boon to natives in India, for though fuel is dangerously scarce, sunshine is not. Surveys show that the sun shines for an average of 310 days a year. This means hot meals about six days each week.

We need not go as far as India, either, to find a need for such a device as the solar stove. A speaker at the first World Symposium on Solar Energy described a village in Mexico where the women walk six miles into the hills for wood to cook with. Paradoxically, there is more than an abundance of sunshine the year round in that location to cook with, heat, and even cool homes when needed!

So far we have talked mostly of "hotbox" or oven-type solar stoves. The skier's stove mentioned earlier is another kind of cooker—a reflector. Instead of trapping warm air inside a closed box, the reflector simply focuses the rays from a large area onto a small spot to heat a cooking vessel of some sort.

In Japan where rice is the staple diet, it is not surprising to find solar rice-cookers. One popular type is composed of numerous small, flat mirrors, arranged to form a cone. Reflected sunlight strikes the blackened surface of the rice pot and cooks the cereal inside.

Just as a properly shaped lens makes all rays passing through it converge at a focal point, a reflector concentrates a large quantity of *warmth* to make a small amount of *heat*. The surface of the reflector is curved, so that the sun's rays strike it at an angle and rebound toward a common center point.

Association For Applied Solar Energy

RICE COOKER manufactured by the Goto Company of Japan. Flat mirrors are mounted inside a wooden framework and adjusted so that they reflect the sun's rays onto the blackened cooking pot. This cooker will boil a quart of water in about 30 minutes. Solar stoves are especially useful in countries like Japan where fuel is scarce.

To make these rays meet in the tiniest point possible requires a parabolic shape, which is a specially computed mathematical curve. Searchlight reflectors and high-temperature solar furnaces must be made in this manner and are very expensive. However, fortunately for those who would cook with sun heat, a spherical shape is good enough for all practical purposes. In fact it is even better than the parabola, since such a perfect reflector would develop enough heat to burn a hole in the bottom of the cooking vessel!

Using the spherical, or perfectly round reflector, gives a larger spot of lower temperature. The simplest solar stove of this type is one made at the University of Wisconsin. It is literally scooped from the sand, a sort of modern echo of Herschel's earlier hotbox cooker!

A tripod is set up over the spot where a cooker is desired, and a calculated distance from the ground. A string is hung from the tripod with a curved scraper attached to its end. With this scraper a depression is scooped from the sand or soil, the result being a spherical hollow. A thin coating of cement is laid over this and then aluminum foil applied to form the reflecting surface.

Ideally the hole is scooped in a south-facing hillside with a slope of about 15 or 20 degrees so that the reflector will be approximately at right angles to the sun's rays. A post is sunk in the center of the depression and a grill attached to hold the cooking vessel. The grill, of course, is placed at the focal point. This is easily calculated since it is half the radius of the sphere.

Crude as this reflector seems, it functions and will cook a meal. Such a solar stove costs next to nothing and has been suggested as a possibility for inhabitants of depressed

University of Wisconsin

A SIMPLE REFLECTOR stove scooped from earth and lined with foil. This is one of many low-priced cookers developed by Dr. John Duffie and other researchers at University of Wisconsin. The depression was formed by suspending a wooden paddle above the soil, using a string of the correct length. Such a stove is not very portable and is best suited to cooking the noonday meal.

areas. There is one limitation; it will operate only at one time of day, say for cooking the noon meal.

The University of Wisconsin has experimented with a number of other types of solar reflector cookers which cost from five to nine dollars for material. One design uses fibreglas, molded over a form in much the manner that boat bodies are. The resulting shell is lightweight and durable. Its inner surface is lined with reflecting material and fitted to a suitable base. Such a cooker would be a good project for scouts or home craftsmen.

One unusual cooker is made of inflated plastic material. It is believed that this design has possibilities for mass production, and besides being cheap it would be easily portable. For all its flimsy appearance, such a cooker will boil a quart of water in twenty minutes or so and cook food in proportionate times.

The average reflector stove is about forty inches across, and not too difficult to carry around. These have cooked everything from bacon and eggs to chicken. All that is necessary is to adjust the reflector so that the hot spot falls on the bottom of the cooking vessel. Every 15 minutes or so it will be necessary to move the reflector slightly to follow the sun. And the cooker will function from sunup to sunset.

As mentioned before, a blackened cooking pot will be more efficient, since black absorbs instead of reflecting the heat from the cooker. While it is possible to fry meat handily, a pressure cooker makes a better companion piece for the solar reflector stove because it does not let the heat escape into the open air. One word of caution in case you come into possession of a solar cooker: The

Association For Applied Solar Energy

DR. MARIA TELKES demonstrates her solar oven by preparing hamburgers. The extended reflectors send sunlight through the glass top of the oven. Temperature inside is 450 degrees, and this type of solar stove can store heat for cooking after dark.

focal point may be in the neighborhood of 1,000 degrees so be careful!

We have talked of the folding, umbrella type cooker and it is obvious that such a device is easier to pack than a rigid aluminum or fibre shell. A Lebanese delegate to the U.N. has designed a folding aluminum cooker that goes into a small container. This feature does not affect the performance of the cooker, and it has fried eggs in Central Park in December. The stove has been produced in Egypt, and its inventor feels that mass production would permit a price of about ten dollars.

A solar researcher in India designed a compact one-piece stove in 1952 and had it produced by a factory in quantity. It cost fourteen dollars, which unfortunately is a large sum of money in India. Besides this disadvantage, there are two others. One is the cooling effect of the wind in cooking outdoors, and the other is the task of educating the Indian people in the use of such a modern device.

This is the solar stove of today, novelty to some and possible blessing to many others. Researchers at the University of Wisconsin have set themselves a goal of a cooker developing 500 watts at a price of not more than five dollars. These devices can make it possible for nomadic peoples in the world's wastelands to prepare hot meals and beverages where it would be otherwise impossible.

There are men who foresee the day when solar energy collectors on the roofs of our homes will cook our meals in remotely heated, built-in ovens. When that day comes we may smile to recall the "old days" when cooking with gas was really something!

CHAPTER
FOUR

Solar Furnaces

In the preceding chapter we talked about sun-powered cookers. Now we come to the solar stove's big brother—the solar furnace. This device, reminiscent of the fiery furnace of Biblical times, is the most spectacular use of the sun's heat.

Magicians use mirrors to create illusions, but solar scientists produce an even greater magic. Today, shiny curved mirrors are doing research and even industrial chores like melting metals previously unmeltable, and creating fertilizer from nothing more than pure air and sunlight!

Remembering that the surface of the sun is a terrific 6,000 degrees C., it is indeed fortunate that such heat does not reach the earth. The record temperature for the most sweltering day is a mere 125 degrees or so. However, by concentrating the sun's rays on a smaller area, we can increase the temperature. With a magnifying glass enough heat can be generated to start a camper's fire or carry out a prankster's joke.

The solar furnace is a refinement of previously mentioned devices. If lenses are used, these are of highest optical quality. Curved mirrors, instead of being spherical, are in the shape of a paraboloid. This "perfect" shape focuses the gathered heat into the tiniest focal point with the result that very high temperatures are available.

Since no instrument is truly perfect, the sun furnace does not quite match the heat of the sun's surface which is the absolute limit in theory. Temperatures reached are amazing, nevertheless. Already scientists have recorded higher readings than the oxy-acetylene torch, and they believe that with better furnaces temperatures perhaps as high as 4,000 C. can be reached!

Reviewing feats of earlier solar researchers, we discover that Cassini melted iron and silver more than two hundred years ago. Diamonds had been melted, and Lavoisier achieved more than 1500 degrees C. These men did wonderful things with the tools at hand, but it was not until this century that a really high temperature solar furnace was built.

In 1921, a modern furnace was made in Germany using silvered-glass mirrors. The precisely ground reflector produced a temperature of more than 3,000 degrees C. This introduced something new by using an auxiliary mirror to reflect the sun onto the parabolic mirror which was fixed for easier handling of experiments. The auxiliary mirror, called a heliostat, tracked the sun as it moved across the sky.

California Institute of Technology built a fine solar furnace in 1932. Instead of using a single mirror the California furnace employed nineteen lenses, each two feet in diameter. This array of lenses gives a total collecting surface of nearly sixty feet, and temperatures higher than 3100 degrees C. have been reached.

Association For Applied Solar Energy

SOLAR FURNACE operated by California Institute of Technology. One of the first furnaces built in this country, it is used in the high-temperature research program of California Institute of Technology.

The first industrial use of the solar furnace came in 1940 with a ten foot mirror built for the AC Spark Plug Division of General Motors. Since optical glass was critically short at that time due to World War II, the mirror was spun from $\frac{1}{4}$ inch thick aluminum and then polished. Also developed was a sliding tube which controlled the temperature at the focal point of the furnace. At present this furnace, the largest in the country, is being used for research in high-temperature aircraft materials.

In our modern world there is a growing need for higher temperatures. The fields of metallurgy and chemical synthetics are good examples. It is therefore understandable that industry is much interested in the possibilities of the solar furnace.

There are ways of reaching very high temperatures with arc furnaces, electrical and electronic methods, and the experimental "shock wave" technique. However some of these yield their peak temperature for only a split second. One arc device which has been suggested for industrial use has an efficiency of only 1%, besides the fact that the electrodes create magnetic and electric fields. They also get in the way, and contaminate the metal being melted.

The solar furnace, on the other hand, can be sustained all day long or at least while the sun shines! There is no soot, no ash, no harmful electric, magnetic, or chemical action. A solar furnace is extremely safe to operate, and for a final reason the power supply is free for the taking. Almost two hundred years ago Lavoisier noted prophetically these advantages which have stimulated current interest in the furnace. Fortunately, today republics recognize the need for scientists.

Builders of high-speed aircraft and missiles are vitally

United States Air Force

SOLAR FURNACE MODEL built by the United States Air Force. At right is a movable mirror which follows the sun as it crosses the sky. On the left is the parabolic mirror which focuses the sun's heat into the "furnace room" hidden back of the mirror. The venetian blind arrangement in the middle is called an "attenuator," and serves to regulate the light admitted to the curved mirror. This controls the heat at the focal point.

concerned with high-temperature research. With airplanes approaching the 2000-mile-per-hour mark and huge missiles traveling at speeds more than double that, the so-called "thermal barrier" poses a problem engineers must overcome.

Many materials have been tried in the solar furnace and found wanting. At temperatures achieved only in the furnace—or in actual flight conditions!—wing leading edges and other parts explode, melt, and even simply evaporate. Then engineers must come up with a substitute that will stand the strain of the heat barrier. This same sort of work is being done in the field of "cer-mets," or materials composed of metal and ceramic bonded together.

Besides the aircraft corporations, many other organizations are already using solar furnaces. Kennecott Copper Corporation has installed a small one at its works in Salt Lake City. General Electric has used a solar furnace to purify phosphor for communications equipment.

The Government's Bureau of Mines maintains a furnace in Morgantown, W. Va., and the Sandia Corporation uses one in high-temperature research work. The Army's Quartermaster Corps is building a large solar furnace, and the Association For Applied Solar Energy intends to erect one in Arizona.

For some time schools have been interested in the furnace as a research tool. California Institute of Technology has been mentioned; there are many others. Fordham University operates a furnace, and MIT uses one to study the effects of radiation on materials. At Arizona State College at Tempe, the first heliostat-equipped furnace in this country has been installed. It is doing research under government contract.

Association For Applied Solar Energy

THIS FIVE-FOOT Convair Solar Furnace, being demonstrated by B. I. Davis, a thermodynamics engineer with Convair, San Diego, California, is constructed of a surplus searchlight mirror, and is capable of attaining very high temperatures in the neighborhood of 3,000 degrees C.

All around the world, everywhere the sun shines, there is interest in solar furnaces. Australia, India, Russia, Algeria and France are among the countries doing solar furnace work. Symposiums have been held, and one university has offered a course in utilization of solar energy. All this points to the growing importance of the solar researcher, the "heliotechnologist," as he is coming to be called.

The ten-foot solar furnace, though the largest in the United States, is small when compared with some in other countries. Algeria, for example, has a furnace approximately 26 feet in diameter. Besides doing research in the high-temperature field, this single-mirror furnace makes fertilizer by the process of fixation of nitrogen from the atmosphere! Thus the sun not only makes crops grow in Algeria, it fertilizes them as well.

Russia has a large furnace, perhaps over 30 feet in diameter, constructed of reinforced concrete and powering a steam plant. But to France goes the honor of operating the world's largest and most advanced solar furnace. This seems no more than fair, with the long history in sun research France has as a heritage.

High in the Pyrenees mountains, in old fort Mont Louis, Dr. Felix Trombe headed the building of a huge, 35 foot diameter reflector which generates 75 kilowatts of power and melts more than 200 pounds of metal at a time. This is truly an industrial furnace, since for 30 days each year it produces metals and refractory materials for French firms.

Experimenting at first with searchlight mirrors, scientists became convinced that a large furnace would be an

Association For Applied Solar Energy

THIS SOLAR FURNACE, one of the largest in the world today, is operated in Algeria. One novel use for it is the "fixation" of nitrogen from the atmosphere. The nitrogen thus produced is used for fertilizer. Notice the mounting that permits the reflector to turn, instead of being fixed as is the case with France's 35-foot furnace. The furnace shown here needs no auxiliary "heliostat" mirror.

asset to the French National Center of Scientific Research. The problem of constructing a one-piece mirror of the size wanted presented an impossible task physically as well as financially. The solution was found in using 3,500 separate mirrors, curved to proper shape with adjusting screws. As mentioned before, these mirrors were made by the St. Gobain glass works which provided the lenses for Lavoisier so many years ago.

The curved reflector made up of these small mirrors is fixed in a vertical position. At some distance from it is a flat mirror, the heliostat, which moves slowly during the day and thus positions the sun's rays on the curved reflector. Although the small mirrors used are not of the finest optical quality, the furnace achieves temperatures above 3,000 degrees C. The focal point of this furnace is a fairly large spot, 4½ inches in diameter.

Used with the huge reflector are rotating containers in which metal to be melted is placed. These spin at speeds of up to 750 revolutions per minute and are cooled by a water jacket. All this is necessary so that the molten metal will not in turn melt the sides of the container!

Alloys or other materials produced in the Mont Louis furnace are extremely pure, since there is nothing to contaminate them. A technique used successfully is that of placing material to be melted inside a pyrex or quartz flask. It is then melted in a vacuum or gaseous envelope, since the sun's rays pass right through the glass.

Supplementing the large furnace are several smaller models. Some of these are mounted horizontally, which makes it easier to melt powders. A carriage mounted on rails is used for this purpose, slowly advancing the material

CLOSE-UP VIEW of the 35-foot-diameter French solar furnace at Fort Mont Louis. This large reflector is made up of 3,500 small flat mirrors, each bent to a slight curve. Heat gathered by this furnace is equal to 75 kilowatts of power, and melts loads of a hundred pounds of metal or more.

into the focal point. With the curved mirror lying flat there is plenty of "elbow room" for such procedure.

An unusual sidelight at Mont Louis is a freezer operated by the sun. It seems strange that the same hot rays that melt materials such as zirconium also can operate a refrigeration unit, but there is much promise indicated in this direction of solar research.

The solar furnace can melt at three fourths the cost of an equivalent arc furnace, and if used solely for industrial purposes the 35-foot mirror would have paid for itself in five years. Although the furnace obviously functions only during sunlight, it is operated more than 2,750 hours per year. Even when there is snow on the Fort, the furnace draws sufficient heat from the sun.

So successful is this giant that France is building one that will make the Mont Louis furnace seem tiny—a mirror 120 feet across! This great installation will have a power of 1,000 kilowatts, or the equivalent of a 1300 horsepower generator, and Dr. Trombe feels that it will melt metal industrially at half the cost of electric arc methods.

Scientists in our country are so interested in the big French furnace that a team has studied the plans and the work as it progresses. The United States Air Force has announced plans to erect a furnace of the same size—120 feet—at Cloudcroft, high in the New Mexico mountains. Models of this proposed furnace include a shutter interposed between heliostat and curved mirror to regulate the temperature at the focal point.

A research organization has suggested furnaces of 50 to 100-foot size for the iron and steel industry, and perhaps someday the solar foundry will be a reality. The solar fur-

Earl S. Ream Photo

THIS LARGE SOLAR POWER PLANT was built in 1903 in Arizona by A. G. Eneas. Its cone-shaped collector, about 30 feet in diameter and composed of a large number of small mirrors, focused heat on a boiler. The steam generated drove an irrigation pump. Notice the glowing boiler tube made of glass, and also the water pouring from the pipe at lower left.

Association For Applied Solar Energy

THIS LARGE FURNACE, possibly 35 feet across, was built by the Russian Heliotechnical Laboratory in Tashkent. The square tank at the top of the picture suggests that this installation is used to generate steam power. Another type of reflector is seen in the lower right background.

Earl S. Ream Photo

THIS LARGE SOLAR POWER PLANT was built in 1903 in Arizona by A. G. Eneas. Its cone-shaped collector, about 30 feet in diameter and composed of a large number of small mirrors, focused heat on a boiler. The steam generated drove an irrigation pump. Notice the glowing boiler tube made of glass, and also the water pouring from the pipe at lower left.

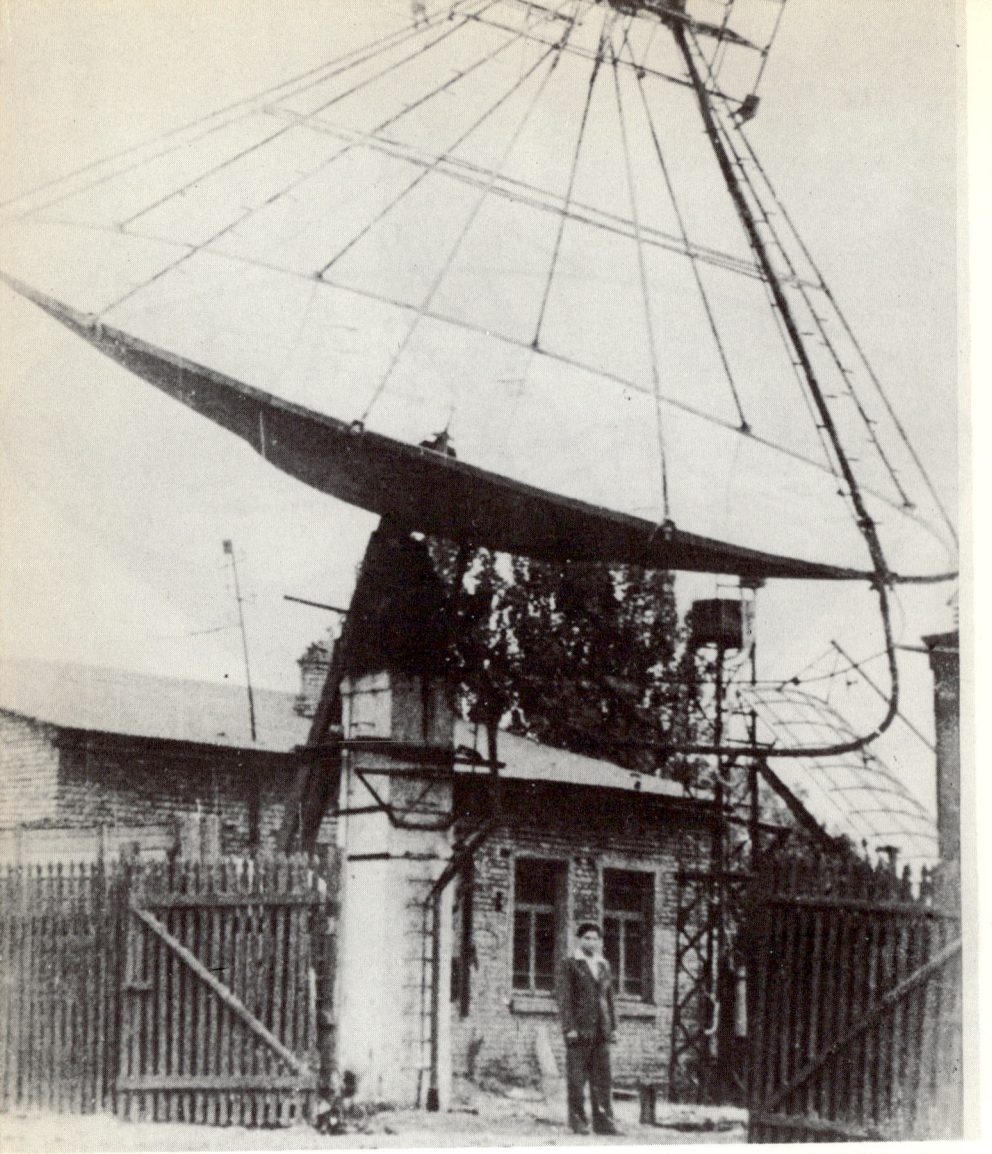

Association For Applied Solar Energy

THIS LARGE FURNACE, possibly 35 feet across, was built by the Russian Heliotechnical Laboratory in Tashkent. The square tank at the top of the picture suggests that this installation is used to generate steam power. Another type of reflector is seen in the lower right background.

nace has already proved it can deliver higher temperatures than any other practical method; it may well invade the general melting field. Though it has the drawbacks of unwieldy size and large initial cost, it has advantages to offset these:

There are no parts to wear out on a solar furnace; the Mont Louis mirrors have withstood six years of weathering and suffered no ill effects even in gales that damaged slate roofs in the nearby town. Even more important, the power is free. As someone aptly quipped, the solar furnace is the hottest thing in the industry!

CHAPTER
FIVE

Solar Air Conditioning

It has been accurately stated that civilized life, as we in this country think of it, would be impossible without house-heating. Anyone who has run out of fuel in midwinter in the northern United States can appreciate this fact. Keeping ourselves warm is so important to us that we use somewhere between one fifth and one third of all our fuel for heating. Each year we dig into our reserve supply the equivalent of nearly one half *billion* tons of coal for this purpose!

Power engineers point out that besides diminishing our stockpile, such use of fuels is wasteful and inefficient. To heat our houses requires only relatively low temperatures; conventional fuels would be much better used in producing high-temperature energy. The sun, however, is the ideal solution to the problem of space-heating, and such an application of solar energy has already proved itself today.

So optimistic are the experts that the President's Materials Policy Commission has predicted the solar-heating of as many as thirteen million dwellings in the United

States by 1975. Even assuming that solar energy could save only half the fuel now spent on heating, this economy would add twenty-five or thirty years to our fuel reserves.

Even in winter, the sun's rays will warm us. Houses with windows facing south gain considerable heat in this way. By very simple means, solar scientists can step up the degree of heat so that the sun can take over the job ordinarily done by gas, oil, or electricity. Since each home can collect its own solar heat, there is no dependence on a central power station or transportation system that can break down just when needed most. Neither is there any loss of energy in transmission, as is the case with power lines.

Solar water-heating is no novelty. For a long time man has recognized this phenomenon and applied it. Rice paddies in the Orient are often irrigated with water allowed to flow in a shallow trench before contacting the plantings. Such warmer water results in better yield. Another example of solar water-heating is the evaporation of shallow ponds to produce salt.

From these simple beginnings it is not surprising that man progressed to heating water for domestic use. The solar water heater was a common sight in California and Florida the early part of this century. At first the tank itself was placed so the sun would strike it and thus slowly warm the contents. Later the idea of coils of pipe made for a faster-heating system. Finally the pipes were blackened to absorb even more heat, and the whole business was enclosed in glass to take advantage of the glass-house principle we have mentioned before.

While these early water heaters were usually poorly engineered, they functioned fairly well. It was only the

THE SOLAR SHINGLED HOUSE OF 19?

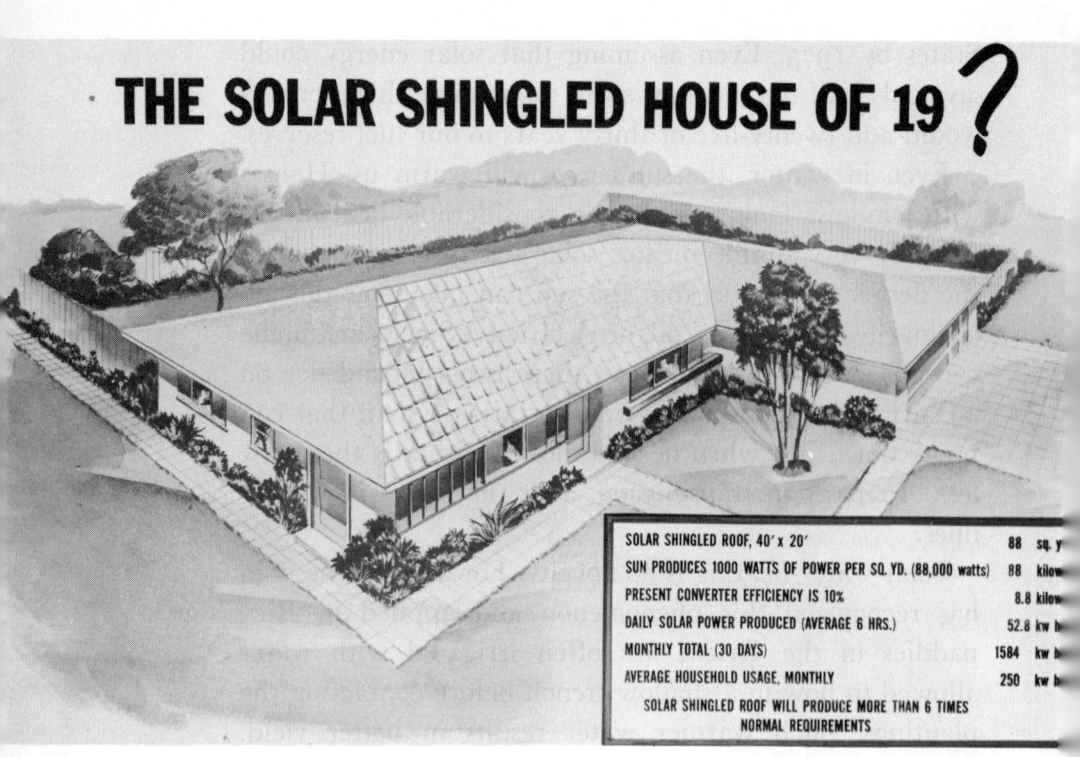

SOLAR SHINGLED ROOF, 40' x 20'	88 sq. y
SUN PRODUCES 1000 WATTS OF POWER PER SQ. YD. (88,000 watts)	88 kilow
PRESENT CONVERTER EFFICIENCY IS 10%	8.8 kilow
DAILY SOLAR POWER PRODUCED (AVERAGE 6 HRS.)	52.8 kw h
MONTHLY TOTAL (30 DAYS)	1584 kw h
AVERAGE HOUSEHOLD USAGE, MONTHLY	250 kw h
SOLAR SHINGLED ROOF WILL PRODUCE MORE THAN 6 TIMES NORMAL REQUIREMENTS	

Hoffman Electronic Corp.

HOUSE OF TOMORROW. This solar-shingled house, deriving all of its power needs from solar cells on the roof, was forecast as a future application of solar energy by Hoffman Electronics Corporation, Los Angeles. The 40x20 foot roof section, shingled with silicon solar cells, would enable the roof to supply 8.8 kilowatts per hour in sunlight. In this manner, only five days of sunlight per month would be needed to develop the proper energy to operate the home.

inconvenience of having bad weather interrupt the hot water supply, and the cheapness of fuel that caused the wane in popularity of the solar heater.

With the introduction of automatic washers, dishwashing equipment, and the need for more hot water, power consumed in water-heating may now be as much as one fourth of the space-heating requirement. Interest in the solar water heater has revived. In 1951 it was estimated that Miami, Florida alone had thousands of such installations. These ranged in size from fifty gallon capacity in private homes to thousand gallon units in apartment buildings. Even though the engineering was not always the best, these heaters generally paid for themselves in from four to seven years. Besides this is the even more important fact that they saved large amounts of conventional fuel.

Today researchers have devised more efficient collectors and worked out proper designs. A collector about seven feet square will provide sufficient heat for a fifty gallon storage tank, and water passing through seventy feet of coils is raised 30 degrees F. Overnight storage is possible, but in areas where there are days of bad weather, supplementary heating methods are of course necessary.

The town of San Remo, Italy, boasts of a brand-new solar water-heating installation. Work is being done in Australia, Russia and many other countries towards more efficient equipment. Some lands which do not have the technological facilities we enjoy have worked out simpler methods. In India, researchers imbed water pipes in concrete for a much cheaper installation.

Besides being economically competitive with conventional types of water heating, the solar heater offers hot water in places where it would otherwise be unavailable—

remote communities, mountain cabins and the like. Solar research has also devised a better way of warming water in swimming pools! This is done by covering the pool with a transparent plastic which admits light but prevents evaporation losses.

Having the sun heat our water is well and good, but stepping from a hot bath into a frigid house would be little comfort. Let's consider how the sun may also heat the house as well. In the first chapter it was mentioned that the roof receives, and wastes, far more energy than all our appliances use in the form of electricity. Solar space-heating offers an excellent way to put the roof to work as a collector for the heating plant.

Normally, most of the heat energy bombarding the roof is reflected back into the atmosphere. In fact reflective shingles are designed to do just that, to waste heat energy so that our homes will be cooler in summer. Later on we will talk of how this heat can be used to refrigerate the home in summer; right now let's stick to the heating problem.

By replacing part of the usual shingles or other covering with glass-plate collector, the solar engineer "soaks up" sun heat. Air is circulated through the collector and then through a normal duct system to warm the rooms. The temperature of this air varies from about ninety degrees in the morning to as high as two hundred degrees at mid-day. Obviously this latter is far more than is needed, and thermostatic controls keep the house from over-heating. Later we will see what becomes of this surplus heat.

In actual tests it has been found that one hundred percent solar heating in a cold climate requires a very large collector, therefore most engineers set themselves a goal

Black Star

LARGE SOLAR water heating installation being completed atop apartment building in San Remo, Italy. Water is piped through coils underneath the special glass plates shown and its temperature is raised as much as 70 degress. A large storage tank will take care of night requirements.

of about three-fourths solar heat, with the balance made up by supplementary heat in the form of gas, oil, or electricity. For this purpose a collector of about six hundred square feet has been found ample for a house with fifteen hundred to two thousand feet of floor space. Either roof or wall can serve as collector, and both types have been used.

A logical question comes to mind when we think of solar heating. What happens when the sun goes down, or when it fails to shine for some time; does the homeowner don his overcoat and mittens? Fortunately this is not necessary, nor must he turn on the gas furnace either. During the day, surplus heat has been stored up. At night, or during cloudy weather, this stored heat is drawn upon to warm the house.

There are a number of ways to store heat. One method is to fill a bin with gravel and pass the surplus warm air over it. After dark, the direction of the airflow is reversed, and the gravel gives back its heat for warming the house! Some designers feel that water is the ideal storage medium and provide a large storage tank which connects with the system. Yet another idea is to use a material which melts when heated to a certain point and stores a large quantity of heat in this manner.

One early solar heated house was constructed by researchers at MIT in 1939. The MIT designers used the water tank storage system. This house, and a second, were purely for testing purposes. However, a third house, built in 1948, has been lived in continuously by student families. Solar heating takes care of three fourths of the needs of the house.

In 1948 another solar-heated house was built at Dover,

Association For Applied Solar Energy

THE DOVER SOLAR heated house. The large second floor "windows" are really heat collectors. During the day surplus heat is stored in containers of Glauber's salt which hold five times more heat than an equivalent volume of water. After dark this stored heat is called on to warm the house. The Dover house gets 95% of its heating from solar energy, despite cold Massachusetts winters.

Massachusetts. One innovation was the use of containers of Glauber's salt for heat storage. This material holds five times as much heat as an equivalent volume of water, and proved the feasibility of solar heating over periods of several cloudy days. The Dover house has furnished up to ninety-five percent of the required heat from solar energy.

Another solar heated house was tested in Boulder, Colorado. A small bungalow, equipped with a roof-top heat collector and a storage bin of gravel, effected a fifty percent saving in fuel. The designer plans a larger home in Denver which employs a collector of six hundred square feet to provide three fourths of the heating.

In Arizona, an architectual firm has constructed a home entirely heated by solar energy. A further development uses part of the same duct and storage system to partially cool the house in summer. The idea of using the sun's heat for cooling in mid-summer is an intriguing one and much work is being done in this direction.

An example of solar energy being used for heating on a large scale is a beautifully modern office building in Albuquerque, New Mexico. This structure has 4,300 square feet of floor space, and one whole wall is formed by glass collector panels.

Heat storage is provided by a 6,000 gallon underground tank in winter. The sun is expected to provide ninety percent of the heat for the building. In the summer time "heat pumps" help to cool the building. An interesting feature is the ability of the system to remove heat from the air during the daytime in spring and fall, store this heat and use it at night to warm the building!

In the scorching heat of summer, solar energy sounds like the last thing we would want. However clever engi-

Rose Photo

FIRST COMPLETELY solar-heated office building in the world. This modern structure was designed and built by the firm of Bridgers & Paxton in Albuquerque, New Mexico. As shown, one entire wall is of glass, backed by metal coils. Water circulates through these coils and is warmed by the sun. Part of it is used to heat the building, and any surplus is stored in a 6,000 gallon water tank buried underground. At night and on cloudy days this surplus heat is used.

neers are working on methods of putting the sun to work operating refrigeration plants! Although this sounds fantastic there is actually a greater potential here than in winter heating.

As a heating source, the sun shines its hottest when it is least needed but the reverse is true in the case of refrigeration. At mid-day, when cooling is most necessary, Sol delivers the greatest power. Efficiently used, this power can keep us comfortably cool in the hottest weather. Thus a six hundred square foot collector atop a home would provide enough refrigeration to cool it in summer.

Strangely, the idea of cooling with solar energy dates back at least as far as 1889. In that year Tellier proposed using a "hotbox" collector to power an ammonia refrigeration system. More recently, in 1938, a scientist suggested burning hydrogen to power a refrigeration system. He would obtain the hydrogen from water decomposed by solar energy.

Besides the mechanical refrigeration plant there is another type known as "absorption cooling." Although not in general use, this absorption technique is excellently suited to solar energy and would require only half the collector area per ton. Thus the six hundred square foot collector which would comfortably warm us in winter would provide up to five or six tons of refrigeration at mid-day. This would be ample cooling for a house in the hot southwest regions of our country.

Experiments have been made with a third type of cooling, a glycol de-humidification process which would be efficient when coupled with a solar energy collector. This type would be most effective in a humid climate, and has

Association For Applied Solar Energy

THIS HOME, belonging to Japanese scientist M. Yanagimachi of Tokyo, is air-conditioned the year round by solar energy. The large screen is a flat plate heat collector, and provides warmth during winter, and power for cooling in summertime.

Association For Applied Solar Energy

RUSSIA, TOO, is active in solar heating experiments. Shown here is a water-heating collector which supplies a bathhouse. Blackened coils can be seen beneath the glass cover. The collector is placed at a slant so that the sun's rays will strike it nearly perpendicularly during the hottest part of the day.

the added advantage of removing unwanted moisture from the air.

While not many of us will move into a completely solar air-conditioned house for some time, it is logical that there will be rapid development in that direction. Architects are aware of the benefits of designs which keep the sun in mind. Improvements are constantly being made in collectors, like the highly-efficient "selective surface" coating developed by Israeli scientists.

Although a solar-heating plant now costs more to install than a conventional type it will break even in about fifteen years. With volume production, costs may possibly be brought down to equal other types.

CHAPTER
SIX

Something New Under the Sun!

So far we have considered the sun principally as a source of energy for stoves, furnaces, and house-heating devices. For years, however, men have cocked an eye toward Sol and dreamed up literally every idea under the sun. Archimedes' solar weapon has been mentioned, as has De Bergerac's space machine, and these only scratch the surface. A glance at patents granted in this country will give an indication of the range of solar inventions.

In 1852, Ulysses Pratt patented a solar ivory-bleacher. Apparently there were huge quantities of ivory needing bleaching, for by 1883 four more patents had been granted for such contraptions! Of course ivory was not the only thing to be dried by the sun.

One early patent, issued in Civil War days, pertained to the curing and drying of fish. Raisins and other fruit also were treated in this manner. As late as 1920 a patent was granted for a solar fruit drier, and more recently, in 1950 as a matter of fact, two patents were allowed for solar treatment of Irish moss.

Association For Applied Solar Energy

THIS MODERN SOLAR CLOCK is a far cry from the sun dial! The collector seen on top of the clock converts light into electricity, driving the motor, and also storing power for use after the sun has set.

SOLAR-POWERED HIGHWAY FLASHER. Continuous operation at night is assured by means of storage cells which hold power obtained from the solar cells during the daytime.

Hoffman Electronic Corp.

Branching out in another direction, one inventor came up with a solar brick-drier in 1883. Applying this technique to another building material a present-day inventor in India has designed a sun-heated lumber kiln. Perhaps one of the most unusual applications of sun driers was that made specifically to bleach feathers way back in 1878!

The year 1881 saw the patenting of a method of warming and ventilating apartments with the sun's heat and this has been a favorite of inventors ever since. Water heaters are popular too. Some researchers were far more advanced, however. As early as 1897 there was a patent granted for the generation of electricity by sun heat on "thermo" batteries. This device was evidently a crude forerunner of the modern solar battery we are familiar with.

Sun pumps and other types of motors date back to 1880 in patent history, but along with these were more homely applications of the energy from the sun. In 1898 a man named Rieke patented the first and apparently the only combination solar stump-burner and insect exterminator!

In 1917 a patent was allowed for a solar solder-heating tool. This interesting use of sun energy is repeated today in an improved device which a home craftsman can easily build and with which he can obtain temperatures as high as 2,000 degrees. There are other applications of the solar "kiln" which we will discuss later on in this chapter.

Although the solar still was known and used in the latter half of the nineteenth century, it wasn't until 1919 that the first American patent was granted. Since then there have been many improvements, including the inflatable plastic stills included in survival kits of aircraft flying over the ocean. The solar still is a simple project, made from inexpensive materials, and can provide distilled

how the BELL SOLAR BATTERY works

SILICON CRYSTAL

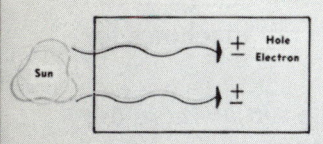

Light is absorbed in a silicon crystal by liberating free-to-move negative charges, called electrons — and free-to-move positive charges, called holes.

ELECTRIC FIELD

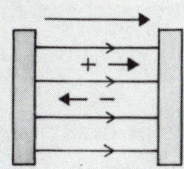

An electric field exerts a force on charged particles causing them to move if they are free. The force moves holes in one direction and electrons in the opposite direction.

SILICON P-N JUNCTION

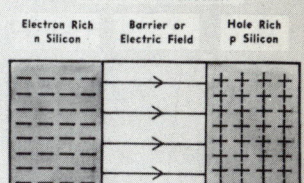

In a thin barrier at the junction between an electron-rich n-region and a hole-rich p-region in a silicon crystal, a strong built-in electric field exists which keeps the electrons in the n side and holes in the p side.

When light is absorbed liberating electrons and holes in the barrier region at a p-n junction, the built-in electric field forces the holes into the p-side, making it positive, and the electrons into the n-side, making it negative. This displacement of the newly-freed charges causes a voltage to appear between the ends of the crystal, a voltage that is a source of electrical power. Thus light energy is converted into electrical energy.

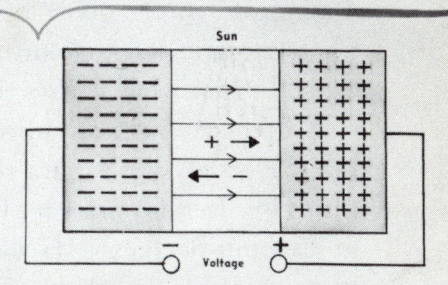

Bell Laboratories

water for a number of uses. Recently a French researcher has suggested a solar *sterilizer* for water.

For a long time the sun has been a symbol of health, and inventors have not slighted this phase of its uses. In 1934 a "solar ray therapeutic apparatus" was patented. There have also been "sun ray heat cabinets," and "cocoon sun sweat suits," as well as solar ultra-violet ray machines for the treating of food.

There seem to be as many uses for the sun as there are inventors to think them up. In 1945, for example, solar patents granted ranged from preparation of green dye to the artificial production of thermal currents in which to fly sailplanes! Reminiscent of the mystical opening and closing of temple doors by the sun centuries ago is the photo-electric cell that turns lights on when the sun sets, and off again when it rises the following morning.

A French scientist studied the possibilities of using the sun to electrify the Sahara region, a place of sun, sand and little else. Jobs for Sol vary from the heating of bath water at Colomb-Bechar, a fact accomplished, to a proposed trans-desert railroad powered by solar-generated electricity. Other Frenchmen believe the only sensible approach to using solar energy is that of somehow tapping the difference in temperature of surface ocean water and water at a depth. Although this is far afield from what we generally consider solar energy, it is the sun of course that heats the sea.

While an Indian factory produces solar cookers, an American manufacturer is seriously studying the possibility of a sun-powered motor for boats! For the outdoor man there is also the solar radio. This is already on the market, equipped with a small solar battery instead of a

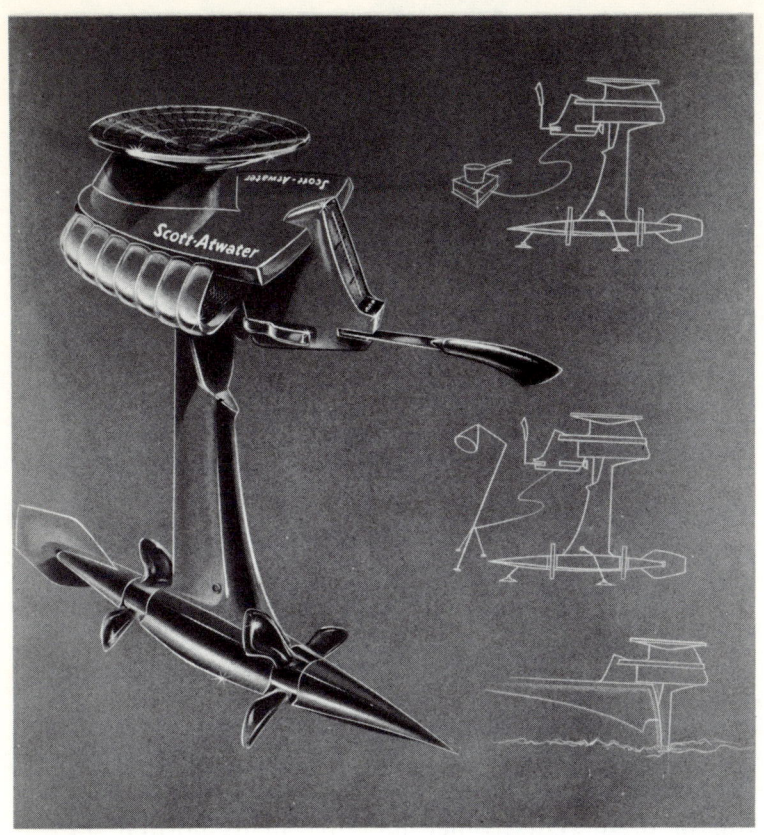

Scott-Atwater Mfg. Co., Inc.

THE SUN WOULD provide the fuel for this solar "dream" outboard motor, conceived by a leading manufacturer. Sun's rays would be trapped by the concave disk and converted to energy that could be stored for long periods. Not only could the solar motor be used for powering a boat, but also for operating camping equipment.

conventional power source, and able to store up power during sunlight so that it can play after dark.

Time and the sun are almost one and the same. In the beginning, man simply divided the day into light and dark. Gradually he learned to tell time more accurately with a sundial. Today there is a solar clock, made in Switzerland, which tells time to the second and needs no winding. Using only sunlight, the solar clock will run continually.

Besides heating homes, the sun has been made a farmhand by doing the same for barns and chicken houses. Solar pumps can provide water, and solar stills purify it if it is brackish. Fertilizer literally "from the sun" has been described. For ages the sun has made things grow, but solar science can make it grow them better. Reflectors, tilted beds and heat-retaining caps for plants are a reality. Dye which makes for better operation of the solar still can also melt snow faster so farmers can plant earlier in the year!

We have talked about solar furnaces of many types, but perhaps the most unusual is that employing a parabolic mirror of mercury. Since mercury in its normal state is liquid, the problem of forming a parabola of such a material seems insurmountable. The solar scientist simply rotates a vessel of mercury, however, and physical laws cause a depression to form!

The same phenomenon can be observed by simply turning a pan of water, though of course in the application mentioned above accurate control results in precise focus and temperatures. The Japanese have applied this principle to an economical process for forming plastic parabolic reflectors. Liquid plastic is poured onto the surface of the water as it rotates. Surface tension spreads the

Hoffman Electronic Corp.

HERE THE SUN is used to drive the propellers of a model plane. Eight solar battery cells on each wing change sunlight into electric power. While such a small collector surface would not provide sufficient energy to fly an airliner, solar batteries could be used to operate auxiliary equipment such as radios, fans and so forth.

plastic, and it hardens into exactly the shape required! These reflectors are used in solar research.

Modern as this technique seems, it actually dates all the way back to 1900. The method is described in a book appropriately called "A New Century of Inventions." As in every science, ideas appear long before they are able to be put into practice. Da Vinci's parachute is a good example of this, coming long before there were any airplanes. In our time, however, we are seeing the result of all the work done in the past.

The photovoltaic process, which changes sunlight into electricity, has long been known. When you use a lightmeter, for instance, you apply this principle. As recently as 1935 experts could not work up much hope for such a method of using solar energy because the selenium cell was a very inefficient converter. "Until something fifty times as good comes along," they said, "we can't consider the sun a power source."

Something similar to this happened in the field of aviation. Authorities flatly stated that five hundred miles an hour was the absolute top for aircraft. Today's planes, traveling nearly three times as fast as sound, prove how wrong this conclusion was. New technology, better fuels and materials change our entire concept. The same thing has happened in the photovoltaic field.

Where once a fraction of one percent was the best a converter could do, silicon discs now turn into electricity eleven percent of the sun's energy striking them. Bell has proved solar batteries can provide part of the power for telephone lines. There will be many other uses.

A dozen photoelectric cells power a toy automobile. There are also model trains, airplanes and even an air-

Hoffman Electronic Corp.

SOLAR BATTERIES run model train. Scientists have suggested the use of such collectors, installed along the railroad right of way to drive full size trains. At present, solar batteries are too expensive for such an application, but research is constantly lowering the price.

craft carrier driven by solar energy. Mechanical magazines give plans for hobbyists to build solar motors and portable radios. In one application, a small square of selenium photocell turned a motor at 400 revolutions a minute, developing one watt of power.

A solar generator in the form of a one-eighth inch square of cadmium sulfide has been made to drive a small motor, producing one third of a volt of electricity. There is a serious drawback at present to using such a motor industrially, because the materials are expensive.

The silicon used in the solar battery originally cost up to $400 a pound, enough to make anything but laboratory experiment out of the question. It is well to remember, however, that aluminum once cost $500 a pound, in a day when a dollar was worth much more than now. Silicon is plentiful, and improved methods have already lowered the price to $180; perhaps further reduction can be expected.

Solar energy makes ice at a laboratory in Tashkent, Russia, and is used in a sewage disposal plant in Tucson, Arizona. One firm is experimenting with paints and wallpapers which "soak up" sunlight during the day, and then give it off at night. No job is too big or too small for the sun!

Artists and craftsmen have long applied powdered enamels to metal by heating to high temperatures, and now some of them work with a solar-fired kiln instead of the usual electric oven. The solar kiln makes use of a plastic Fresnel lens to focus the rays of the sun into a small crucible of firebrick.

Such a kiln can be made for a few dollars and is an interesting project for home or school. Its use is simple,

Mellmann Photo

USING THE SUN to "fire" enameled jewelry, the artist has placed a copper shape, coated with enamel powder, in the brick oven. It glows brightly because the lens at the top of the wooden frame focuses the rays of the sun into it. The "hot spot" is brilliant enough to require the use of welding goggles, and melts and fuses the powder to the metal.

requiring only that the sun be focused properly. Wearing goggles to guard against the glare of the 2,000 degree hot spot, the artisan places the metal to be fired in the crucible. The high temperature flows and bonds the powdered enamel to the copper shape; giving effects not attainable with regular firing methods.

Another use for the kiln is in silver soldering, brazing and other operations. The home craftsman can build such a device for very little, getting excellent results since the solar heat is pure and uncontaminated as has been noted before.

One inventor made a cigarette lighter of dubious merit by simply placing the cigarette through a flashlight reflector. This is perhaps the most trivial use the sun has been put to, in comparison with tasks like operating a huge still as large as an acre in area. But big job or small, the sun is impartial, pouring down its allotted heat on each square foot of earth.

Each day there does seem to be something new under the sun, some fresh application of solar energy. Where once we had a handful of men working separately to harness the sun, now international organizations promote the exchange of ideas and industry backs the research necessary. Many branches of science have a stake in further knowledge of the sun, and they are working together toward that goal.

The big fireball in our sky is a challenge, and the waning woodpile gives an added urgency as man turns to the sun. Ages ago we were born of the sun; today we live in the sun. When we at last reach out into space it may be solar energy that lifts our ships from earth.

CHAPTER
SEVEN

Food and Water from the Sun

So far we have talked of the sun as a means of providing power to take the place of fuels that are slowly running out, and as a means of heating homes and possibly cooking our food. But what of the food itself? The same inescapable pressures that make the fuel experts worry about the future are producing a nightmare for those concerned with feeding our fast-growing population. Every day there are 60,000 new mouths to feed, and a shiny new solar stove will be a grim joke if the cupboard is bare!

We commonly think of huge storehouses filled to overflowing, and grumble about surpluses. The truth is that two years of drought, similar to the actual happenings of the 1930's, could wipe out our surpluses of grain and other foods. A member of the Senate Agriculture Committee recently stated that production of food is running only three or four years ahead of population.

The United States is one of few lands having more than enough food. In many places it is already nip and tuck between appetite and food supply. The prospect of tripled population within a hundred years underlines the fact that of all the fuels the most vital is fuel for us humans, our food. Here again we are dependent on the sun, and to the sun we must look for the improved methods of crop-growing needed to keep us alive.

Photosynthesis, the growing process of plants, is still a secret only nature knows. Somehow chlorophyll is able to change water, carbon dioxide and energy into carbohydrates and oxygen. Carbohydrates, of course, are food. So what we eat is literally manna from heaven, beamed to us through ninety-three million miles of space.

The magic of photosynthesis is the most efficient conversion of sunlight into chemical energy and changes about a fourth of the sun's rays into something we can use. However, this ratio is a theoretical one obtainable only under laboratory conditions. Under actual growing conditions some plants are only one tenth of one percent efficient. Sugar beets, the best, turn only two percent into food, and the average is about one-half percent.

Agronomists, crop production experts, are understandably interested in increasing the yield of crops, and much progress is being made. Better strains have been produced and scientific use of soil and fertilizers helps too. More recent techniques include tilting seed beds so that the sun strikes them more squarely, and using reflectors and heat-retaining caps over plants.

One ingenious trick, mentioned earlier, involves applying dye to spring snow to cause faster melting. Hydroponics, the growing of plants in chemical-filled gravel beds, shows promise and experiments have been made with stacking such beds one above the other to make more use of available ground space.

Association For Applied Solar Energy

ON THIS EXPERIMENTAL farm in California, the seed beds have been tilted so that the rays of the sun strike them more directly. The increased heat energy results in higher crop yield. Paper reflectors help use solar energy more efficiently.

All these devices are steps toward increased production, and in laboratory conditions the yield of beets in Holland has indicated the possibility of harvesting up to forty tons of dry plant material per acre per year. This is so much more than the normal crop that it makes exciting news. However it is still in the experimental stages and it will be a long time before such results are common.

Even the most advanced of these techniques requires proper soil, fertilizers and weather conditions. These factors limit considerably the land available for the raising of food for the world, and already we can see the cultivation of practically every square inch of land as in Japan, Okinawa and other places. Because of this another kind of "farming" is being seriously considered to make better use of solar energy so we will not starve in the years to come.

In 1951 the Carnegie Institution in Washington asked the research firm of A. D. Little, Inc. to build a pilot plant for the cultivation of a very unusual crop. Instead of tilled soil, this "farm" consisted of 600 square feet of plastic tubing, with water circulating through it. The "plant" was a tiny organism known as *chlorella pyrenoidosa,* actually algae such as forms on the surface of ponds!

Resembling some strange chemical racetrack atop a factory building, the *chlorella* "farm" was fertilized by carbon dioxide gas and converted sunlight into food in a most satisfactory manner. With figures obtained from three months of operation, the firm was able to predict yields of up to 35 tons of dry algae per acre per year, far more than is achieved with conventional crop-raising methods.

The advantages of such a crop are immediately obvious. In the first place, with a much higher efficiency of conversion, *chlorella* culture yields several times as much food

A. D. Little, Inc.

CHLORELLA, an algae culture, is grown in this rooftop "food factory." Water circulates constantly through the oval shaped plastic container which admits the rays of the sun. Carbon dioxide is added, and the algae multiply rapidly. Unlike other crops, this is a continuous operation. In Japan, chlorella is already used as a food.

per acre of farm. It needs no rich soil, and in fact can make use of wasteland. Freezing and heavy rains would not be the danger they are with ordinary plants.

Chlorella is much higher in protein and fat content, as well as in the amount of vitamins. Besides this advantage, every bit of the yield is usable since there is no stalk, root or leaves to be wasted. Added to these advantages is the fact that there are no weeds!

Finally, *chlorella* requires only water and carbon dioxide for rapid growth, and can be cultured continuously. This makes the farming operation approach the highly efficient level of industrial mass-production. Very little human attention would be required; the farm would be a sort of automation in agriculture.

Although the starving man of the future would be likely to pay any price for food, it is interesting to know the cost of the finished product. Engineers have estimated that in a large-scale operation the dry product should cost about twenty-five cents per pound.

Interestingly the Japanese have reached about the same figure in their experiments. *Chlorella* production in that country has reached the point that actual foods are being made from it. At the twenty-five cent figure, *chlorella* is only twice the cost of soy beans, the cheapest protein available in Japan.

Compared with eggs, *chlorella* costs only half as much per pound, and only one fifth as much as milk. With meats, the new food compares in price to whale meat or squid, both of which are popular in Japan.

If we are to some day enjoy a diet of *chlorella*, its flavor should be of some interest to us. It is here that the product loses out somewhat, since powdered *chlorella* looks like

Association For Applied Solar Energy

THIS RUSSIAN fresh-water solar still produces about 250 gallons of water a day. Such a device permits use of salt water or water that is otherwise undrinkable.

De Wald Photo

SOLAR SCIENTIST Dr. George Löf with drawing of solar fresh water still envisioned by the Department of the Interior. Installed on the seashore, such a system could use the tides themselves instead of pumps. Salt would be a useful by-product.

green tea, and tastes a little like seaweed! Human ingenuity can work miracles in this field too, fortunately, and Japan already has sampled candy, soup, and even ice cream made with *chlorella* powder. The soup is said to be even more tasty than the popular "Miso" soup which is made with fermented soy beans.

The suggestion has been made that *chlorella* be fed to animals since they are not as fussy as humans in these matters. This has been done in the United States, and also in Germany, though of course the high price makes it uneconomical except as an experiment. Chances are good that by the time it becomes necessary to subsist on *chlorella* foods they will be quite palatable, since hunger is surely the best sauce!

Japan is more pressed for food than we are, and she has done more work in the field of *chlorella* culture. In attempts to reduce the cost of the "farm" Japanese scientists have experimented with culture on open ponds or tanks. This has been fairly successful, except that the dust must be removed occasionally, and once in a while a cannibalistic culture invades the *chlorella* and eats up the entire crop in a day or two!

There are difficulties to be worked out, of course. The plastics used thus far are subject to brittleness and cracking after a period of time. *Chlorella* culture uses 4,000 tons of water per ton of crop, compared with 1500 tons of water per ton in conventional farming. But necessity is said to be the mother of invention, and when the need is food itself, we may expect that these details will be overcome. A farmer may someday merely turn a valve and start a pump to harvest his crop.

While it is natural for the hungry man to turn to the

sun for food, we generally think of Sol as making us thirsty and certainly of no help when we crave water to drink. Oddly, the sun will provide fresh water in the middle of the ocean as downed aviators can attest. For this purpose another solar device is used, the solar still.

The whole world is a giant water-purifying system, as a matter of fact. Sun heat evaporates water, principally from the oceans, and this eventually condenses in the form of rain. Salt and other minerals are excluded in this process, a phenomenon that gives us seasoning for our food. Water, food and seasoning all come from the sun.

It seems paradoxical that a man can go thirsty in the middle of an ocean of water, but unlike fish we cannot subsist on salty water. Large ships have distilling plants, but it was not until World War II that solar stills for use at sea came into being in any quantity. The result was a plastic, inflatable and floatable bag which evaporated sea water, then condensed it so that it was drinkable.

A simpler version consists of black toweling, the end of which is dipped in the salt or brackish water. Such stills have been made by students in grammar school science classes, but it is this same principle that furnished up to 6,000 gallons of fresh water in a place appropriately named Las Salinas in the mountains of Chile.

This huge still, covering 51,000 square feet of area, was built 85 years ago and made habitable an area that otherwise would have been wasteland. Interest is high today in like systems for obtaining fresh water in many parts of the world. In Israel, for example, the Solar Radiation Laboratory has worked out a project for supplying fresh water, using solar stills fed from Red Sea salt water.

Even in our own country, some sections are already

Association For Applied Solar Energy

SAILORS USING plastic fresh water stills. These lightweight, inflatable solar stills operate solely on the sun's heat and produce enough fresh water to sustain a downed flyer or shipwrecked sailor.

troubled by water shortage. Arizona is interested in the possibility of using Gulf of California water for irrigation. Of course such water must be de-salinated, and the solar still would be an excellent answer.

So important is the adequate supply of water that the Department of the Interior has let contracts for construction of large solar stills. A still, one acre in size, built of concrete, has been designed. A test model, one tenth this area, is being installed at San Diego, California, converting Pacific Ocean water into something more drinkable.

While the initial cost of a large solar still is high, there is little in such an installation to wear out. It is possible that the tide itself can fill the evaporating chambers so that no power will be required for pumps. A useful by-product in the form of salt makes the idea more interesting. The fact that such a water system operates only during daytime has been pointed out, and also that it will not distill when it is raining. However, at such time it will at least collect rainwater which is already fresh!

In places where there is an abundance of fresh water available at low cost, the solar still is not likely to appeal. There are presently two large fuel-operated distilling plants, one at Kuwait, Arabia, on the Persian Gulf and the other at Curacao, Dutch West Indies. These yield one million and two million gallons of fresh water per day respectively. Cost of construction was approximately six dollars per daily gallon yield.

In comparison with these fuel-operated plants, a solar still would cost between two and four dollars per daily gallon initially, and then deliver water for about one third the cost. Such figures indicate that there is a bright future ahead in the field of water purification by solar energy.

Association For Applied Solar Energy

THIS LARGE SOLAR still, covering an area of 51,000 square feet, was built in Las Salinas, Chile, in 1872. Available water was undrinkable, but the still provided 6,000 gallons of pure water a day with no operating expense. Heat trapped under the glass plates evaporated the brackish water and the vapor condensed on the slanting surface of the glass. Fresh water ran into a trough and then to a storage tank.

CHAPTER EIGHT

Power from the Sun

It is estimated that the whole world uses approximately five billion horsepower, with the United States accounting for one billion of this total. With the prospect of "running out of gas" in the near future, what will we do about it? There are two obvious choices. Either we must learn to live much as the cave men did, or we must find ways to continue the delivery of power in the huge quantities to which we are accustomed.

It has been suggested that vegetation could be used as fuel when coal, oil and gas are gone. Calculations show that roughly six billion horsepower could be developed in this way, more than enough to drive the wheels of industry. However, we would starve to death as a result.

The idea of growing algae and burning it for fuel has also been advanced, but here again such a product would be far more useful as food. A man having a choice between a meal and an auto trip will probably choose the meal, so fuel experts feel we must look elsewhere for motive power.

Besides the fossil fuels there are a number of so-called "eternal" power sources. One of these is the internal heat of the earth and in rare instances this force has been put to work. Italy has made slight industrial use of this phenomenon, but more frequently we hear of it as the destructive, uncontrollable might of a volcano. Harnessing such energy is a doubtful prospect.

The energy of earth's rotation is tremendous, but it too is difficult to apply to our needs. Gravity, a mysterious power that no one entirely understands, may someday furnish useful work. Several organizations are studying gravity, and "g-engines" have been talked of.

Even the most optimistic researcher does not offer either of these last two energy sources as a practical answer to the power shortage. With all possibilities explored, including fission, which may help industrially while the material lasts, and fusion which seems more suited to engines of war, we turn again to the sun. Solar energy has been rightly called our only "income energy," and on that we must live when the legacy left by nature is gone.

Fortunately the sun is bounteous with her gift of energy, because earth is a prodigal child. Fully a third of the sun's rays are reflected back into space and lost forever. The natural process of rain-making is an expensive one, using 20,000 times as much power as we humans require for all our needs!

Of course we need rain for many reasons, and we do salvage some power from earth's weather factory. With dams and hydroelectric plants we trap about 50 million horsepower all over the world. Potentially there is nearly a thousand times this much water power available to us, though requiring a terrific expenditure for huge installations.

The tides, due in part to the sun, offer another possibility as a power source. Some work has been done to put the rise and fall of the sea to good use, but so far such use is negligible. Here again such projects are costly, depend on water, and require transmission of power if it is to be used anywhere but on the shore.

Windmills for pumping water were a factor in the opening of the American west. They are still a familiar sight in many parts of the world, and a picturesque trademark for Holland. Wind-driven generators provide electricity in areas not reached by power lines, but in the United States these generators, and windmills, develop a total of only about 50,000 horsepower. This is but a tiny fraction of our needs, and even exploited to the utmost the wind could not take care of a significant amount of requirements.

In sharp contrast to the power available from wind and water, which are secondary solar sources, is the vast amount of directly available energy. The engineer can draw on two million *million* horsepower! Since present power consumption is at the rate of only five thousand million horsepower, the sun offers hundreds of times what is necessary. Even more important is the fact that it will continue to do so for ages to come.

We have talked of domestic heating with solar energy, but what of the other three fourths of our power needs? Transportation, industry, and electrical generation must be provided with fuel too, and the solar scientist is interested in this supply that is free for the taking.

Taking it is not quite as simple as it sounds. The sun

Association For Applied Solar Energy

DR. CHARLES ABBOT, standing at right, displays his solar engine. This machine, built in 1936, consists of heat collector and boiler, and develops ½ horsepower. In a special demonstration broadcast, Dr. Abbot provided power to the transmitter by means of solar energy.

beams vast quantities of light to us. In this light are particles of energy, bullet-like "photons" which excite molecules of matter they strike. This results in heat, the basic form of power. For over a century this theory of solar engines has been known, and we have described early experiments in the field of hitching the sun to mechanical devices.

Although Ericsson was aware of the limitations of low-temperature solar heat, many wild-eyed inventors thought a small mirror or lens would produce fantastic amounts of power. The truth is that for each horsepower of energy to be developed approximately fifty square feet of collecting surface is needed. For this reason the simpler the collector and generator can be kept, the more likely the solar engine will be practical.

The flat plate collector has been described in the chapter on house heating, and such a system has been considered for use in a large power plant. A solar power station was designed for El Paso, Texas, consisting of acres of flat plate collectors to produce municipal power. This sunny locality receives the equivalent of almost ten million kilowatt hours per acre, per year.

At the time the research was done, it was estimated that such a plant would produce power for about three times the cost of conventional methods like natural gas. Obviously electricity at three times present rates is not attractive and such a project will not be built this year or next.

Since the El Paso plans were made, however, a development in flat plate collectors called "selective surface" coating has been invented by an Israeli scientist. This coating makes the collector much more efficient, and easily produces steam. It is possible that further improvements

Weiner Photo

WILLIAM RHODES, inventor, describes his Novoid solar engine to Dr. Lee De Forest, called the "Father of Radio." In its way, the engine shown here is perhaps as revolutionary as the radio tube which De Forest invented. Heat from the sun is focused on part of engine being pointed out. Steam is generated, and causes a pulsating hydraulic thrust which can be used to drive mechanical devices.

will make solar electricity competitive with that produced by gas or oil plants. At a recent meeting of the American Institute of Electrical Engineers a paper titled "Solar Energy as a Supplementary Power Source" treated the idea as quite feasible.

A figure has been given of fifty square feet of collector area for each horsepower, but this is for a condensing reflector or lens, which also is able to follow the sun during the day. The flat plate collector which has been considered for an electric power station varies in efficiency from excellent when the sun's rays shine squarely on it, to zero at sunset and sunrise.

It is assumed that in practice not more than fifty horsepower per acre can be realized from a stationary collector system. Based on these figures, it would require an area of about 50,000 square miles to furnish all the power needed by the United States. This sounds discouraging at first but when it is considered that land useful for nothing else would suffice, and also that the solar collector might be in the form of roof surface, the picture brightens.

When other than the flat plate collector is used, the efficiency of the solar engine goes up and is limited only by the second law of thermodynamics. This principle states that heat engines cannot be more than approximately forty-five percent efficient. Allowing normal working loss, the solar engine may still show an efficiency of fifteen or sixteen percent and this is more than most mechanical devices.

Italian solar pumps ranging from one tenth to two horsepower have proved themselves. In this country, solar steam plants have been designed which could be built for about 700 dollars per horsepower. Such devices would

Association For Applied Solar Energy

HENRY CABOT LODGE, JR., U.S. Delegate to the United Nations (*right*), inspects a solar engine made in Italy during a visit to Stanford Research Institute. SRI imported the solar engine, which produces 1½ horsepower, for research on its use for drawing subterranean water to the surface in desert and other wasteland areas.

handle most farm chores now done by electricity or liquid fuel engines, and in remote areas where fuel is expensive because of transportation costs, could compete favorably even today.

Another country which has done much in the solar energy field is Russia. The Krzhizhanovski Institute has built many power plants at Tashkent and worked out the design for a full-scale steam-electric solar plant.

Using a central boiler placed on a tower forty feet high, this installation makes use of an idea dating back to a solar researcher in this country in 1903. Large mirrors are mounted on carriages on a circular track arranged about the boiler room. In this manner the mirrors may follow the sun and keep its rays focused on the boiler to generate steam during the hours of daylight.

Russian scientists estimate such a plant would provide 1200 kilowatts of power, and would take care of the needs of a city of fifteen or twenty thousand people, heating their houses in winter and cooling them in summer.

The Russians foresee the use of small solar engines to provide hot water, home heating, refrigeration, fresh water and so forth; as well as large power installations for irrigation, drainage and industrial use. Quite aptly, they refer to this as "heliopower," and predict a need for it in the very near future if not immediately.

In a previous chapter a French plan for a solar-electric railway in the Sahara was mentioned. A similar idea has been suggested for railroads in this country. On either side of the tracks, solar collectors would gather power to drive trains along at no fuel cost! Such electricity would not have to be sent long distances over power lines as it is now,

Association For Applied Solar Energy

DR. FARRINGTON DANIELS of the United States, visiting New Delhi, India, is shown a solar hot air engine by Dr. M. L. Khanna. This engine, which uses a focusing type collector to furnish driving power, was designed and built by the National Physical Laboratory of India.

and would save losses incurred in that way. For nighttime operation, batteries could store up power during sunlight and release it later on.

There are other solar engines already built which offer possibilities. The hot air engine, invented before Watt's steam engine, is ideally suited to solar energy power source. Ericsson built the first solar "caloric" engine in this country in 1872. Only the cheapness of other fuels kept it from being adopted then. Current interest in solar energy has revived work on the hot air engine, and test models have been built in Holland and in India.

The World Symposium exhibited many other solar engines, including an unusual pinwheel arrangement of glass bulbs filled with liquid. A screen shaded some of the bulbs and unequal heating of the liquid caused the pinwheel to rotate.

Another device, similar only in that it too used the sun for motive power, concentrated the sun's rays on a tiny pulsating hydraulic motor. This unique engine has no moving parts and is adaptable to uses ranging from refrigeration to water pumping.

Although skeptics point to the fact that to compete with a large conventional power plant the solar plant would be unwieldy in size, they forget an important fact in the generation and transmission of power. It is true that a station producing millions of kilowatts is more efficient than one producing only a thousand, but frequently transportation of fuel to the plant, and power from it, eats up a good bit of the output.

Solar energy, on the other hand, is available on the spot almost anywhere. Thus a small village might well have its own electrical generating plant powered by sun energy at

Association For Applied Solar Energy

THIS IS AN artist's conception of the proposed Russian solar steam power plant. Movable mirrors on the circular tracks follow the sun and focus heat on the central boiler. Models of this installation have been tested and it is estimated the full-scale plant would develop 1,200 kilowatts of power, enough to heat a town of 20,000 people.

a cost less than bringing in electricity from a distant hydroelectric plant. Even if the price is higher than coal or oil generated power, we must agree that it will be better than no power at all!

Thus far we have talked only of a rather indirect method of changing sunlight into electricity. The sun's heat is easiest for us to use with only simple materials at hand. Photovoltaic conversion—changing sunlight directly to electricity—will be discussed in the following chapter. We will see what makes the solar battery work, and also learn about another amazing possibility for using the sun's energy.

CHAPTER NINE

More Power from the Sun

In October, 1955, a Georgia farmer picked up his telephone and made a call. When he had completed his conversation the farmer smiled and said it sounded just fine. For the first time, direct solar energy had powered the telephone lines near Americus, a town south of Atlanta. The Bell Telephone Laboratories experiment was a complete success.

The device that made this possible was a metal panel about a yard square, attached to the telephone poles. A number of tiny, so-called "solar batteries" converted the sunlight into electricity and furnished this power to the telephone line.

In the last chapter we discussed the conversion of the sun's *heat* into power for various mechanical devices including those which would finally turn it into electricity. We come now to the photovoltaic process, which skips the intermediate steps and makes electric power directly. This fascinating principle offers exciting possibilities in the solar energy field.

As we noted before, something new under the sun is rare. The photovoltaic effect was observed by Antoine Becquerel in 1839. This French physicist was followed in his work by a son and grandson, the latter sharing the Nobel Prize in 1903 with the Curies.

While the first Becquerel laid the groundwork for the conversion of sunlight to electricity, it was 1897 before an American was granted a patent for the application of solar heat to "thermo" batteries.

For a long time there have been two similar devices in use; the thermocouple and the photoelectric cell. The thermocouple relies on temperature difference in two metals to cause a tiny current to flow. It has been used for furnace controls, and also by astronomers to measure the light of stars. The photoelectric cell is best known as applied in the photographic exposure meter.

Both of these conversion methods produced such small amounts of current they were of no value except as controls. The development of a practical photovoltaic converter came about in an indirect way.

The earliest radios, the old-fashioned "crystal sets," used simple semi-conductors as detectors. As radios were improved and the vacuum tube invented, the crystal was all but forgotten. Only as higher frequencies were used did the crystal detector come back into its own. Work was begun in the 1930's that led to the production of transistors, small crystal replacements for the vacuum tube that used only a fraction of the power.

The element silicon was used early in this research, but it was found that germanium was better suited for transistors. However, as a by-product of transistor research, scientists discovered what is known as the "p-n junction."

Bell Laboratories

THE LINEMAN is checking on the operation of a solar battery installed on telephone pole in Georgia. In this experiment, Bell Laboratories proved the ability of solar energy to furnish current for telephone service. Used with storage batteries, the unit shown here can provide continuous power. At present the solar battery is too costly to be used in place of regular power, but research is lowering the price so that some day "sun current" may be economical.

By introducing impurities into silicon, researchers created positive and negative materials between which current would flow.

After World War II, work was intensified on the silicon p-n junction and it was noted that it would be ideal for uses such as solar energy conversion. Between theory and realization there were many barriers.

Silicon, coming from sand, is one of the most abundant materials on earth. But ordinary silicon was of no use for a solar battery. Painstakingly scientists had to learn to "grow" single crystals of silicon, and then purify these crystals. Obviously no one man invented the solar battery. It was the result of long cooperation among many men in many fields.

The first successful solar battery was demonstrated in 1954. The device is credited to three inventors; a physicist, a chemist, and an electrical engineer. The battery itself was a strip of arsenic-treated silicon with a thin coating of boron on top.

While the completed battery looks simple, it is difficult to make. The crystals used in its production still cost about $180 per pound, and accuracies of one ten-thousandth of an inch are required in making the battery. Thus far it is too costly to be considered a replacement for standard power methods, but it must be remembered that the device is only a few years old. In time it should become much more economical.

Each square yard of the earth's surface receives approximately one kilowatt of energy. We have discussed solar cookers which deliver about half this, or 500 watts, to the cooking vessel. At first glance this sounds phenomenonally efficient, until we remember the energy is still in the

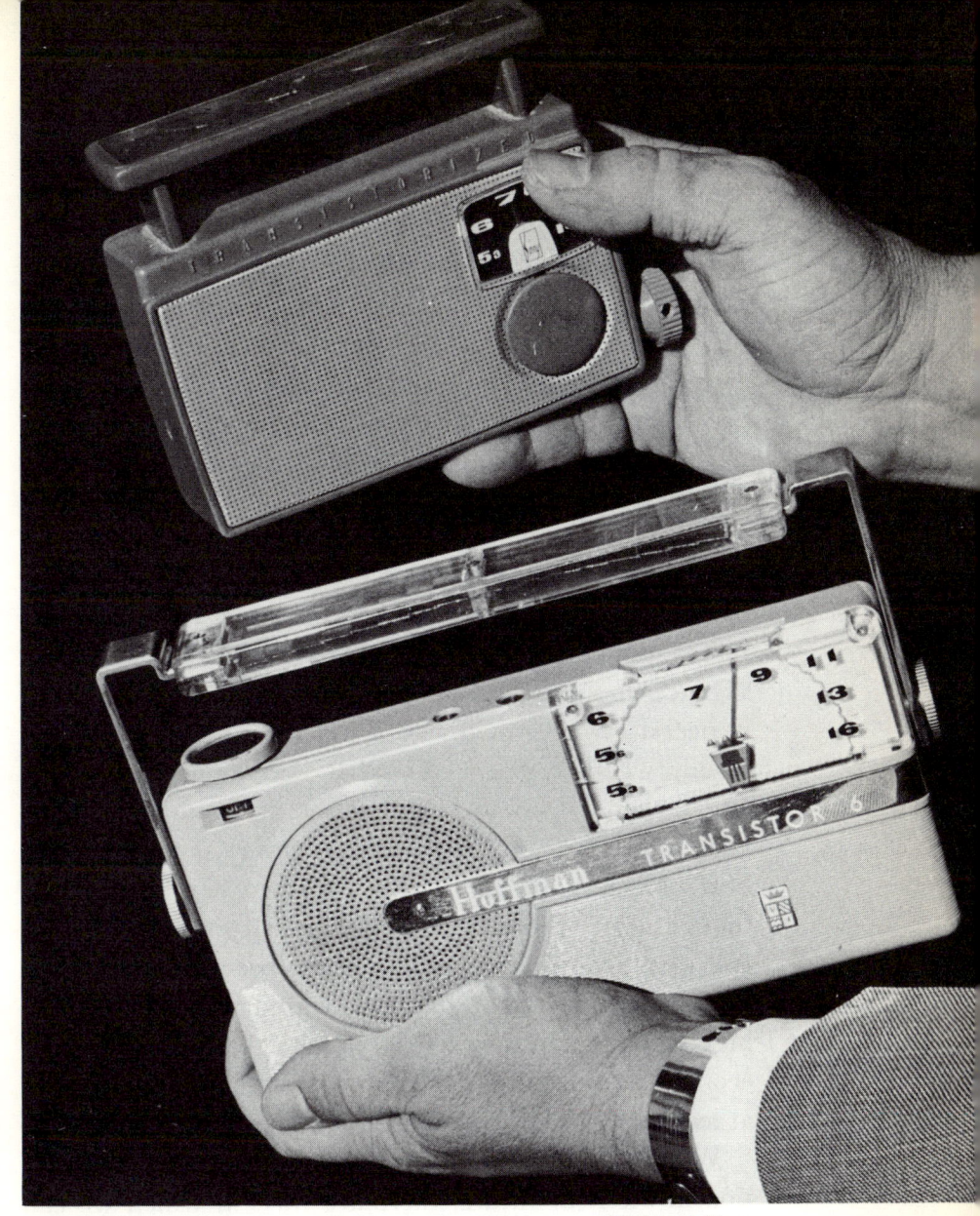

De Wald Photo

SOLAR-POWERED RADIOS. Using transistors, which require very small amounts of power, solar radios operate on current generated in the plastic handle by solar batteries. Surplus current is stored for use when sunlight is not available.

form of heat. Converted into electricity by mechanical means results in only about a hundred watts flowing through power lines.

Scientists believe that a maximum of 22% is possible in photovoltaic conversion. This is because only a fifth of the sun's spectrum gives photons, or "bullets," strong enough to excite the electrons in silicon. The figure of 22%, however, is far above the best of our conventional machines.

Before the solar battery, the best photovoltaic devices delivered only a fraction of a percent of power. The battery demonstrated in 1954 was rated at six percent. In just one year this was nearly doubled, and the batteries used in the Georgia telephone lines converted 11%, or more than a hundred watts per square yard.

Since the solar battery operates only during daylight, it is necessary to provide storage batteries for night and cloudy weather power. This has been done successfully and power is available around the clock, making many possibilities apparent for the solar battery.

If efficiency of the battery were to rise to a figure thought quite probable, installation of 800 square feet of collector area on a rooftop would produce more than enough electricity for lights and appliances. Even at a high cost for installation, the solar battery would be economical since it has no parts to wear out and, in theory at least, will last forever!

While none of us is likely to make such a home installation in the near future, there are ways in which we can put the sun to good use with solar batteries. Firms market radios equipped with solar batteries. For the hobbyist, mechanical magazines have published plans and instructions for solar-powered small motors, and also radios.

De Wald Photo

"BIG BERTHA" of the solar batteries. This panel is made up of 400 cells which convert sunlight directly into electricity. With operating efficiencies of better than ten percent, such converters deliver about 100 watts power per square yard of collector surface. This panel, made by Hoffman Electronics, Inc. is designed to track the sun as it moves across the sky.

A short-range radio transmitter operating on a battery the size of a package of cigarettes has been demonstrated, and such units would be useful for campers, rangers, and as emergency equipment for downed fliers.

As an indication of the wide interest in solar batteries, a number of firms now produce solar cells. Research work is being done using germanium and also cadmium sulfide in place of silicon. An electronics firm has installed batteries in model planes, trains and boats to show the possibilities.

Solar batteries atop our garages could charge storage batteries for use in cars when, or even before, gasoline runs out. The car top itself offers an interesting possibility! There are small electric cars available today, and free battery-charging would make them more desirable.

These are interesting speculations, and as such they only scratch the surface of what may someday be. While it is foolish to say that in ten years the solar battery will be our main source of power, it is certain that it will soon do much more than carry the human voice along a telephone line.

To this point we have been discussing the use of devices for changing sunlight into electricity in one step. We come now to another process which makes use of sunlight. Photo-chemical in nature, this process uses the sun's rays to decompose water into its elements—hydrogen and oxygen. These gases both may be burned as fuel, to produce power from the sun!

Where the agronomist is concerned with photosynthesis, and the electrical engineer with the photovoltaic process, it is the chemist who carries solar research ahead in the photo-chemical field. This is the newest phase of solar

Association For Applied Solar Energy

HOW SOLAR BATTERIES may some day furnish electricity to a power line. Using land that would otherwise be wasted, and requiring no tending, the batteries will convert sunlight directly into current instead of the present method that calls for burning fuel to drive generators. A similar suggestion has been made for railroad rights of way, furnishing driving power for electric trains.

energy work, and while it is still definitely in the laboratory stage it is one of the most challenging prospects the solar scientist has.

For years swindlers have held out the bait of making fuel from water by the addition of a magic "power pill." Many gullible people have been separated from their money by such a rosy dream. Since water is the thing we have most of in the world, a means of using it as a fuel would solve all our problems.

An early step in the solution of this age-old dream was the "Hill Reaction," discovery of a British biochemist. It was found that chlorophyll-carrying bodies when illuminated will accept electrons from water. This was a ray of hope in the search for a way to decompose the water into hydrogen and oxygen, but only a faint ray since the reaction was only temporary.

A Russian physical chemist thought of using compounds other than water, from which it was easier to remove electrons. Here again, though, the reaction was brief, and then the compound returned to its original state.

Massachusetts Institute of Technology scientists have been working on the problem for some time, and have devised a method of adding a coloring agent to water for improved decomposition. Thus they have been able to break water down into its component parts.

Ultra-violet light has been used in these experiments, which means only a small part of the sun's spectrum is effective in the process. In spite of this fact it is expected that the process will have an efficiency of thirty to forty percent, using techniques being studied at Stanford Research Institute.

The chemists working on this problem are optimistic in

Hoffman Electronic Corp.

THE FOUR DISCS showing on the deck of this model carrier are "solar batteries." They convert sunlight directly into electricity and drive the motor in the ship. Notice the wake behind the carrier. Solar energy could not power a ship of this size, but might drive auxiliary equipment and also distill drinking water.

spite of the fact that so far only small amounts of gas have been liberated in experiments. They feel there is no good reason for believing the decomposition process cannot become one of economic importance.

There are two distinct possibilities in the solar photochemical field. First is the breakdown of water into hydrogen and oxygen. Second is the generation of direct electric current in the solution itself.

In England two researchers have proved the possibility of recombining hydrogen and oxygen through a porous fuel cell. This results in water, and also the generation of electrical current with as high an efficiency as sixty-five percent!

It is easy to see how simple it would be to join the two processes for the production of electricity from sunlight. Using realistic figures for both steps in the conversion an over-all efficiency of about twenty-five percent might be realized. This, we should remember, is much higher than the most optimistic prediction for the solar battery.

The English scientists, working at Cambridge University, have operated their fuel cells for a thousand hours. Since the cells and the fuel they use are very light their possible importance becomes obvious, particularly in the transportation field. This method also takes care of the problem of storing solar energy very neatly.

While perfecting the decomposition method will by no means be easy, it is certainly not impossible. The cracking of gasoline by fractional distillation, the production of synthetics, and many other industrial processes now taken for granted were at one time seemingly insurmountable hurdles.

By spending billions of dollars, man has unlocked some of the secrets of the atom. Solar scientists are confident that a fraction of that sum applied to research in their field will yield equally fruitful results, with the added advantage that such results contribute to the maintenance of life rather than to its destruction.

CHAPTER
TEN

The Solar Scientist

It has been only a little over ten years since a fantastic, mushrooming cloud turned the attention of the world to a newcomer in the field of science. This modern expert and the tools he works with were created by the spending of huge sums of money, none of which has yet been recovered except militarily. Even when atomic power plants do begin to send electricity through the wires it is possible that this new technology has a limited life. This is because atomic fuel, like coal and oil, can be used just once.

In contrast, the solar scientist dates all the way back to Archimedes, more than two thousand years ago and his future is bright. It is as though the sun has tried for centuries to tell man to look up, that he must in the end turn to the sky for his power. The solar scientist, far from being a novelty, is one of our oldest researchers.

We have talked of Lavoisier, the martyred Frenchman, and of Ericsson in America. Other men, famous for their work in different fields, were attracted to the sun. Langley built an airplane and also solar devices. Professor Goddard, the father of modern rocketry, patented four solar inventions.

Even Pasteur, whose name has carried over in the process he gave to mankind, worked in the solar research field. Either these men were all far ahead of their time, or the rest of the world lagged behind them. There was no need, or so it seemed, for the direct tapping of the sun for power. When the forests were gone, man could burn coal and oil and gas, couldn't he? And brilliant men would dig further into the earth, or the atom, when those fuels were gone.

Today, man has begun to look toward the sky. At the World Symposium in 1955 it was evident that at long last the sun was being taken seriously. Interest in solar energy burst out with explosive force, seemingly triggered by international gatherings of scientists first abroad, and then in the United States. Where men had once worked alone they now had an association, and journals of their own. Where atomic research was conducted in utmost secrecy and produced tensions that gravely upset the world, solar research enjoyed a free exchange of ideas. Sun energy, as we have mentioned, seems ideally suited to peaceful purposes.

With the distinct possibility of need for solar energy as early as 1975, many of the young people now entering the study of science and engineering may well be the "heliotechnologists" of tomorrow. No wild claims are being made, and obviously a high-school graduate could not go out and find a job as a solar technician.

That same high-school graduate could go on to college and become a solar scientist, however, because the handful of trained people available now cannot do all the work that is ahead. When the Air Force announced it would build a huge solar furnace high in the mountains near Alamogordo, New Mexico, it invited interested college personnel, *or students,* to apply for appointment to the project.

There will be opportunities in this new field—one with a force at its command as far exceeding the atom as that mighty force outstrips the oxcart! It is a challenge to scientifically inclined young people to begin preparing for a task of vital necessity to our growing world. Physicists, engineers, chemists, thermodynamicists and metallurgists are among those who should find a place in solar technology.

Government and industry alike have a keen interest in solar research. Aiding in the recent World Symposium were organizations including the National Academy of Science, Ford Foundation, United States Air Force, National Science Foundation and UNESCO. Stanford Research Institute and University of Arizona helped prepare the program.

In 1956 a symposium on high-temperature research, featuring solar furnace discussion, was held and drew 500 delegates. Their names were a veritable roster of important industrial firms and government agencies. The Association For Applied Solar Energy held its second symposium in January, 1957.

Besides the aircraft industry, interested in high-temperature research for planes which are flying several times the speed of sound, the melting industry has an eye on the solar furnace as an addition to its foundries.

The power industry realizes the importance of solar energy, first probably as a supplementary source and ultimately one of primary significance. Electrical and mechanical engineers number solar researchers among their members, and papers on the subject have been accepted recently. "Solar Engineer" may be a formal title some day!

The effect of the sun in chemistry and in agriculture has been discussed. One interesting application is a laboratory in Arizona for the testing of paints, fabrics, dyes, wire insulation, and many other materials. Interestingly, one measurement of radiation used in these tests is called a "langley," named for S. P. Langley, the pioneer sun researcher.

The director of this exposure laboratory tests everything from plastic pipe to lawn furniture. His instruments include "Marvin sunshine switches" and "pyrheliometers." Besides this, he of course has a thorough background in solar theory and is a practicing solar technician.

The sun is of vital importance in the field of meteorology too, and the French scientist, Lyot, gave a great boost to weather study when he perfected the coronagraph. This instrument permitted viewing the sun's corona and was a great stride in the search for a sun-weather link.

In this country men of the U. S. Weather Bureau proved the connection between sunspots and rainfall. Scientists in Brazil found the same relationship in that country. Today scientists of the High Altitude Observatory in Colorado continue the work. Meterologists use solar observations in aircraft flight planning, another example of how the sun reaches into many phases of modern life.

Communications, the network that makes modern civilization possible, is affected by the sun too. A major part of the observations made during the International Geophysical Year will be made by solar scientists, and the first satellites will take readings of solar radiations high above

DR. C. G. ABBOT, pioneer solar researcher, and Research Associate of the Smithsonian Institute, with a small model of his solar boiler. Using a mirror 10 feet in diameter, Dr. Abbot has shown that two horsepower can be developed by the sun. A boiler of his design is now being tested at the University of Arizona.

Association For Applied Solar Energy

SCIENCE TEACHER points out exhibit to school children, some of whom may become the solar scientists of tomorrow. It is thought that as early as 1975 fuel shortages will be felt throughout the world, and for this reason uses of solar energy are of great importance.

the atmosphere. Another approach to communications has been mentioned in the use of solar energy to power telephones and radios.

Even the architect is concerned with the sun, as is the heating and refrigerating engineer. The process of distillation opens up another whole solar technology too, from the production of salt and fresh water to the disposal of sewage, using sun energy.

It is difficult to think of a field in which solar research is not important. Let us see what it takes to make a solar scientist, and what is being done in colleges and universities. Merritt Kastens, Assistant Director of Stanford Research Institute and much interested in solar energy, has this to say:

"To produce a creative research man in the educational sense, it is necessary to combine a sound elementary orientation in the high school with seven or eight years of university training, and perhaps as much as five years research apprenticeship before profound and significant contributions can be expected. In view of this situation, students now entering high school may be expected to begin to have a significant impact on our industrial technology not much before 1975. The implication is obvious that the men and women who will be called upon to make the greatest strides in solar technology are those now beginning their training.

"This does not imply in the least that active efforts are not now under way to harness the sun's energy, nor that major strides will not be made in this direction during the next 20 years. In fact, one of the most impressive charac-

Association For Applied Solar Energy

SCIENTISTS FROM ALL over the world attend the World Symposium on Solar Energy, in Phoenix, Arizona. Such gatherings, and the forming of the Association For Applied Solar Energy provide for an exchange of ideas in solar research. Interest is increasing rapidly and great strides are being made in this new scientific field.

teristics of the field of solar technology today is the spectacular rate of increase of research effort expended.

"It is perhaps pertinent to point out that even with the current expansion of research activity in this field, total expenditures to date cannot exceed a few million dollars. It is a little disconcerting to compare the state of the art in solar applications after the expenditure of this modest amount of effort with the technoeconomic status of the peaceful uses of nuclear energy after the spending of literally tens of billions of dollars. It is no doubt fruitless if somewhat intriguing to speculate on what might be the state of development of solar technology if equivalent billions had been expended in its exploration.

"However, it seems fairly obvious to me that by the time the current science and engineering students become contributing members of the technical community, there will be an appreciable demand for skills and knowledge in the application of solar power. Contributions from many disciplines will continue to be required to increase utilization of the sun's power. However, just as we now increasingly recognize the nuclear engineer as a special class of technologist, we will probably some day develop the specialized 'heliotechnologist.' "

Until recently there have been no formal courses taught in schools pertaining to solar energy specifically. However in 1950 Massachusetts Institute of Technology offered a session for engineers in the field of solar house-heating. In the summer of 1956 the University of California at Los Angeles gave a course titled, "Utilization of Solar Energy" carrying two hours of credit.

More such courses may be expected with the eventual possibility, as Mr. Kastens pointed out, of formalizing solar

Association For Applied Solar Energy

STUDENT AT LEFT watches solar scientist adjust solar furnace atop Science Building of Arizona State College at Tempe. This furnace, the first in the United States to be equipped with the sun-tracking heliostat at the left, does government research in the high temperature field.

studies. Meanwhile many schools have active programs now in solar research that give opportunity for interested students.

Arizona State College at Tempe, for example, recently installed the first heliostat-equipped solar furnace in this country. This is being used to do research under contract to the government. A 24-year-old physics major had the distinction of being the school's first solar energy student. Along with him, two high school teachers studied and operated the furnace, and will pass on their knowledge to their own classes.

University of Wisconsin has a Rockefeller Grant and works principally with solar cookers, pumps, coolers, and radiation measurements. New York University has a solar program too, including experimental stoves and solar stills.

MIT studies radiation with its furnace, and another project is photo-chemical research which has been described in more detail in the last chapter. Fordham has a solar furnace, and plans a much larger one. The University of Florida includes solar water heater research among its projects.

Stanford Research Institute has a threefold program including photosynthesis, flat plate collectors, and high-temperature research. These are not all of the institutions with active programs, of course, but give an idea of the scope of solar research.

Men in three dozen countries are looking to the sun with an eye to putting it to work for them. Unlike buried fuels which are plentiful in one land and scarce in others, sunshine is generally impartial with its blessings. The so-called "Solar Belt," from the Equator out beyond the

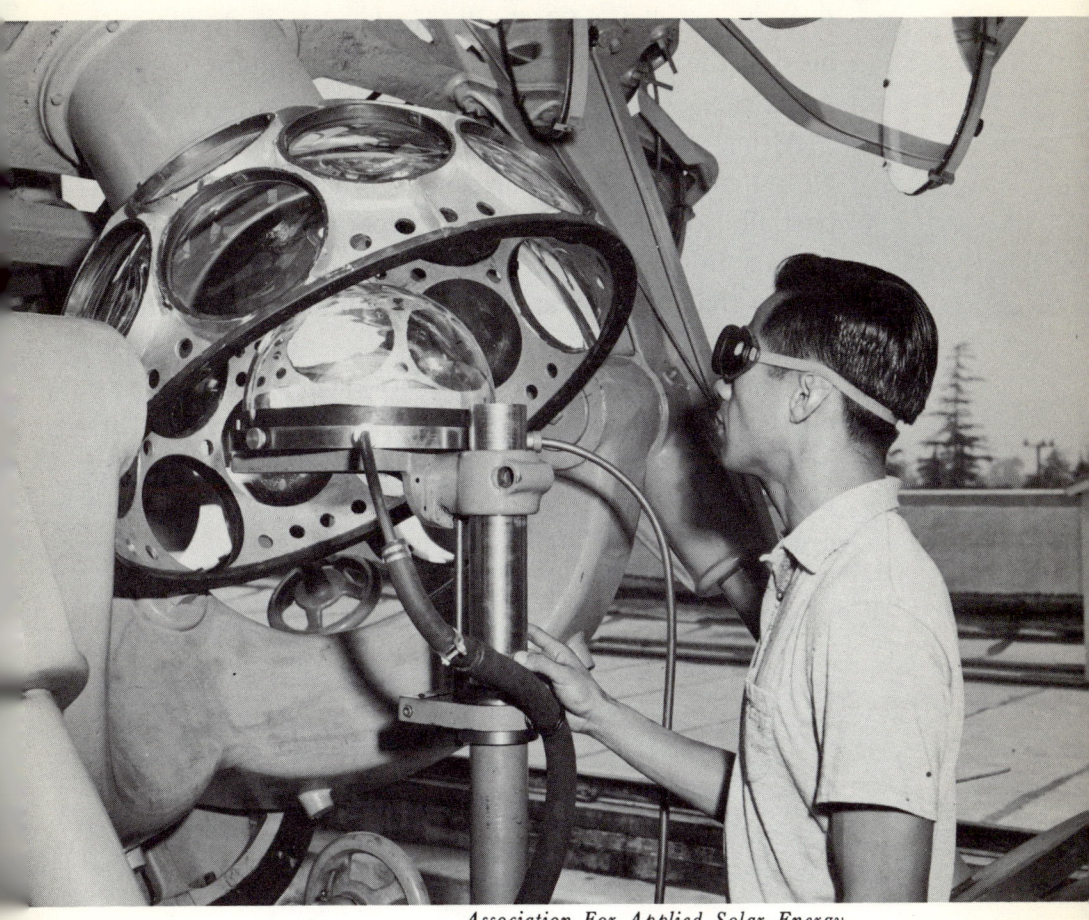

Association For Applied Solar Energy

YOUNG SCIENTISTS like this one operating the large solar furnace at California Institute of Technology are preparing to carry on the research and industrial tasks of the solar energy field. Government and business alike have a keen interest in new developments and offer financial and other aid to the program.

fortieth parallels of latitude north and south, takes in most of the United States. It also includes most of South America.

Africa, Australia, India, China and Spain are countries almost entirely in the solar belt, and many other lands are partially so. The same sun that operates Trombe's huge furnace in the south of France cooks rice in Japan. Solar energy that pumps water in Italy will also fire jewelry in Phoenix, Arizona.

As scientists from many countries exchange information on their latest solar discoveries and inventions they are helping to prove that there is a place in the sun for all of us. And the sun, as we have seen, can provide us with everything we need to live and to enjoy life.

CHAPTER
ELEVEN

Solar-Powered Space Ships

In 1656, more than three hundred years ago, Cyrano de Bergerac described a solar-powered space ship in his "Comical Histories of the States and Empires of the Sun and Moon." At a time when the Pilgrims were just getting a foothold in America, a hundred years before Watt began fiddling with his steam engine, and two hundred years ahead of Jules Verne, who is generally thought of as the first science-fiction writer, Cyrano blueprinted space travel.

The longnosed Frenchman, famous for his writing and his swordplay, was immortalized by Rostand at the turn of the last century as a romantic hero. Cyrano's imaginative foresight was amazing, since he pictures his space craft as a double-walled, hollow cylinder with lenses fitted into the outer surface. These lenses focused the sun's rays to heat air inside, resulting in motive power for the space ship.

Technically the author is guilty of two errors, though we may blame this more on a joking attitude than ignorance. Cyrano must have known that there is no atmosphere in space, and this alone would have grounded his machine for extra-terrestrial flight. Also he described the heated air as rushing out the *front* of the cylinder and thus tugging the craft along with it. Either Cyrano was aware of a principle not yet discovered by scientists today, or his space ship would have flown backwards!

Even with these errors, we must still admire the early writer for his prediction, since as we enter the era of space flight considerable attention is being given to solar power. One example we should shortly see is the use of solar batteries in the earth satellites to be launched.

It has been pointed out that the power available in space will be not the thousand watts per yard we have considered on earth, but nearly half again as much. Even a hundred watts of power is sufficient for the larger, instrumented satellites and would provide energy for radio transmitters, cameras, and other equipment. Since such a satellite will spend much of its time in shadow, however, the solar battery will have to be used together with storage cells to provide continuous power. Another qualification is the possibility of deterioration of the solar batteries by cosmic ray bombardment.

Also speculated on is the possibility of using the fuel cell mentioned earlier, in space travel. Nuclear power is being considered for space flight, but the problems of shielding such a dangerous engine are tremendous. If the nuclear reactor were put in a structure separate from the crew's quarters and fuel cell, the reactor could decompose water into oxygen and hydrogen which would be piped to the space ship proper. There the crew would re-combine them to produce power to drive the entire assembly.

American rocket scientist Krafft A. Ehricke has proposed what comes closer to being an actual solar-powered space ship. Although the picture of this ship does not resemble Cyrano's fanciful creation, there is a technical similarity. The modern design uses a spherical reflector instead of lenses, and hydrogen is burned and ejected rearward. The basic idea is the same—solar heat causing the emission of a driving gas.

The solar-powered space ship was presented in a paper read to the American Rocket Society. It notes that the chemical rocket is hard to beat, but points out that the enormous cost of supplying a space ship with fuel from earth is a serious restriction. Fuel scarcity may well be a more restricting factor than cost, which makes solar energy more attractive as time goes on.

The designer considers nuclear power, mentioning the handling difficulties associated with an atomic pile, and also suggests the possibility of refueling on other planets to lessen the fuel load carried from earth. He believes that the first space travel will be done with chemical fuels, but that ultimately we may use the sun to drive our space craft.

The proposed method, while not 100% sun powered, uses solar energy to replace more than 20 tons of liquid oxygen. Still requiring a quantity of liquid hydrogen, the planned ship would weigh 16,000 pounds and carry a crew of two in a central gondola. The weight of the space ship is thus about that of a fighter plane.

Two huge reflectors, each more than 100 feet in diameter are required to generate the heat for the hydrogen motor, and to construct an assembly of this size, keeping the weight within reason, would be nearly an impossibility. While a parabolic reflector is optically perfect and delivers the highest temperatures this would actually be less practical than a spherical reflector. The spherical shape gives a lower temperature over greater area at the focal point.

Another disadvantage of the parabolic reflector is the unwieldiness of a "dish" the size needed in the space ship. The designer therefore cleverly proposes a complete, balloon-like sphere of plastic. Produced with a thickness of only one thousandth of an inch, the clear plastic transmits 90% of the light striking it. Half the large inflated sphere would be metal-sprayed to form the reflector mirror which concentrates heat on the heaters for the liquid hydrogen.

Filled with hydrogen or helium at low pressure, the huge bag would be cooled as a small amount of gas "diffuses" through it. It is not thought that cosmic dust would make holes large enough to be dangerous.

The smaller spheres at the surface of the clear half of the bag generate electrical energy for pumps and standby power to be used when traveling in the shadow of a planet. The entire assembly can be pivoted to face the sun no matter what direction the space ship is moving.

There are of course many problems involved in such a space ship. The danger of meteor damage is a possibility. Rate of acceleration would be very low, and maneuverability poor. It is felt the design presented here would be useful only for lunar trips because of the limited amount of fuel.

Along with the disadvantages there are advantages however. The fuel, hydrogen, will be readily available in the post-fossil-fuel age. The idea of using the craft as a balloon to great altitudes is intriguing, but the designer suggests ferrying it disassembled to a satellite. Space travel would begin from there, and launching would be much

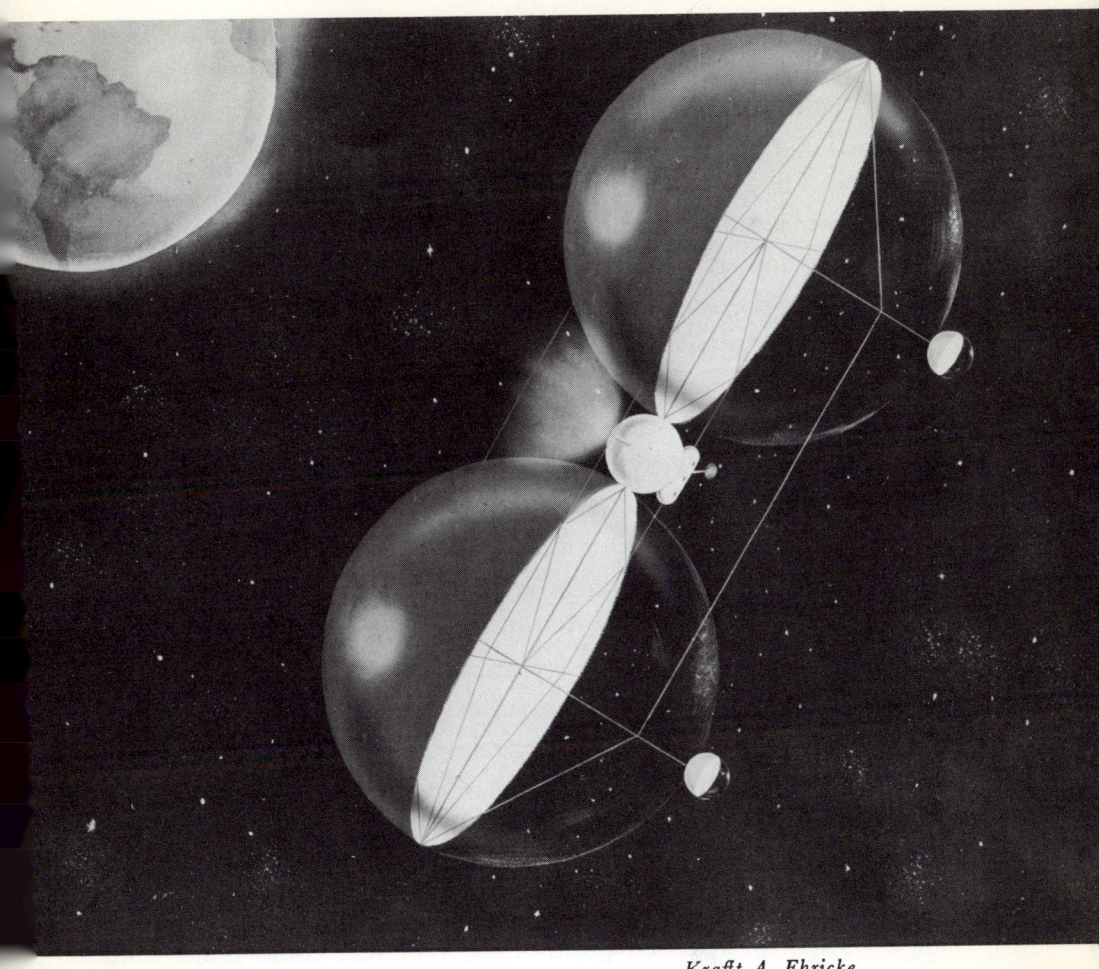

Krafft A. Ehricke

IN THIS PROPOSED space ship solar energy takes the place of many tons of fuel. The two ballon-like plastic spheres are silvered on half their surface to form huge reflectors. Liquid hydrogen is heated by this "solar furnace" and drives the rocket ship. The two small reflectors provide power for auxiliary equipment, pump motors, lights, radio, and so forth. Such a space ship would be very light. Its designer feels it is best suited for moon trips.

safer than conventional high-acceleration methods. For these reasons, *astronauts* may leave earth in a craft resembling the balloons of their pioneering grandfathers, the *aeronauts*.

The proposed space ship uses what might be called a conventional driving motor; that is, it relies on the thrust of a burning fuel. There is another kind of thrust that the space ship designer has thought of, called "photon propulsion." A stream of electrostatic energy emitted from the rear of the craft creates forward movement in this system which is purely theoretical so far.

Dr. Ernest Stuhlinger, who is head of guided missile research at the Army's Redstone Arsenal, has designed such a space ship which he feels could be used for longer voyages through space. While it too uses stored fuel, solar energy is used to heat this fuel and create the emission, resulting in an even greater weight-saving than in the previously mentioned craft.

It is assumed that a large, interplanetary space ship will begin its trip from a satellite of earth, and "land" on a like satellite at its destination. Fuel for the journey would have to be carried from earth to the satellite in rockets, burning up 170 pounds of fuel for each pound deposited at the satellite. Thus cost and scarcity of fuel could make long space voyages prohibitive.

These difficulties led to the idea of an electrically propelled craft. Its engines would use the material cesium or rubidium, which when striking an incandescent platinum surface cause a stream of ions to flow. This ion stream would be accelerated by a negatively charged electrode, making a sort of electronic jet or blast. An example of photon propulsion in our immediate experience is the

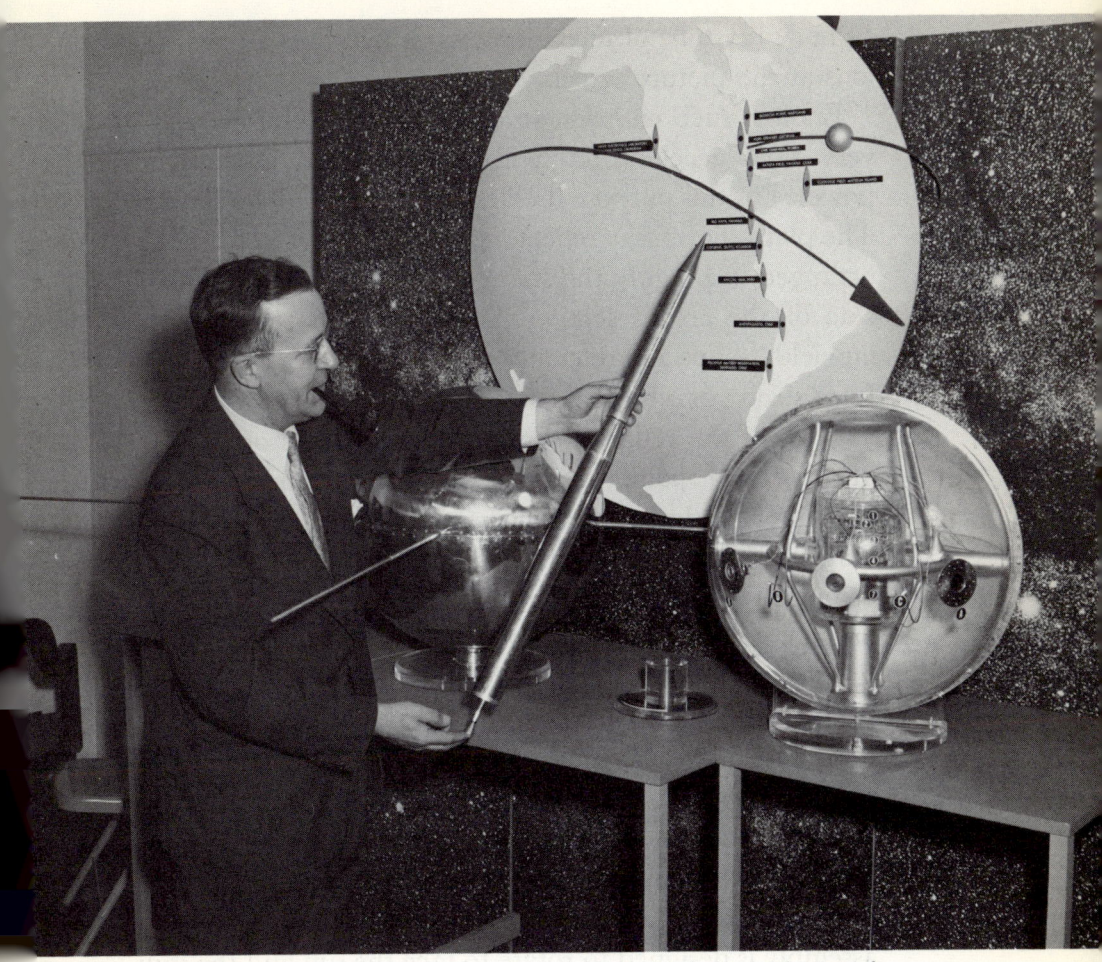

Official U. S. Navy Photograph

DR. J. P. HAGEN, Director of the Vanguard Project, and models of the first earth satellite. First use of solar energy in space will probably consist of solar batteries installed in such a satellite to provide power for radio, television camera, and other equipment.

cathode ray tube of television sets, which fires a stream of ions at the picture screen.

Enough such emission to drive a space ship, even at a very slow acceleration, will require large amounts of power. For this purpose the designer would call on the sun. The plans show forty reflectors, each fifty feet in diameter, arranged in roughly the shape of butterfly wings on each side of the crew's section. Such a design results in an unwieldy shape suitable only for travel in free space away from strong gravitational stresses.

Each of the reflectors concentrates its rays on a boiler at the focal point, and the boiler operates a turbo-generator producing 200 kilowatts of power. A large number of relatively small reflectors are used to guard against crippling loss of power because of meteor hits. There is another reason, too, for the smaller reflectors. It is far simpler to build a fifty foot mirror than one hundreds of feet across.

The turbo-generators supply the 7500 kilowatts needed to create the ion drive, with enough left over to power auxiliary equipment such as pumps, radios and so forth. Streams of ions are emitted from 1,000 propulsion chambers arranged in a honeycomb shape. The entire collector assembly is designed to rotate to face the sun and the individual reflectors turn also to aid in circulation of the liquid used in the generator boilers.

Since so many reflectors are needed, along with the piping for liquids and transmission of power to the center control section of the space ship, there are inevitable losses. Besides this the design is not particularly maneuverable. If the solar battery, with its direct conversion of sunlight to electricity, can be raised considerably in efficiency it would aid in making a more compact craft.

Although photon propulsion has many drawbacks, including a very low rate of acceleration which would make necessary the use of power for half the trip for forward motion and the remainder for braking, it has advantages too. Proof of this lies in a hypothetical voyage to Mars.

Carrying a crew of ten, and a "payload" of 50 tons, the electrostatic space ship would make the trip with only 250 tons of fuel. A conventional rocket ship would require 1100 tons. Even more attractive is a longer flight, and one requiring a time of two years would use up only 275 tons as compared with 7500 tons of "old-fashioned" rocket fuel! The longer the flight, the better for the solar space ship.

Since all this fuel must be ferried up from earth to the satellite at a cost of 170-to-1, the chemical rocket space ship would need 1,275,000 tons of fuel! The electrostatic craft would use 46,750 tons, which is bad enough. It may ultimately be necessary to rely entirely on solar energy for flights deep into space.

It was three hundred years from the fictional space ship of Cyrano to the serious proposals of today's astronautic scientists. How much additional time will be needed for making theory into accomplished fact we cannot say with any degree of certainty. There are many who scoff and sneer at the mention of space travel, unable to understand why men should want to venture off the earth. But the adventurous spirit is strong, men have always had an eye on the stars.

What began with Icarus and Daedalus carried on with the Wrights and Lindbergh. Goddard and Oberth blazed trails in rocketry, trails that looked more inviting as the last frontiers *on* earth fell. Now there are scientists who can put what was once a dream on paper. Tomorrow the blueprint may become reality and men will reach the moon. Beyond that are the planets, and the sun shines on them too.

CHAPTER
TWELVE

The Sun Tomorrow

Up to now we have been discussing the history of solar energy and its status today. Important as these phases are they are the faintest shadow of what is surely to come. If the sun is vital to us now it will be more so tomorrow and each succeeding tomorrow. Where the past and its heritage are the prime factors with the fossil fuels, the future and its promise are the aspects of solar energy we are most concerned with. In this last chapter we will discuss the fruits of research being done today.

At the World Solar Symposium, a speaker told the gathered scientists something he heard from an Indian in Canada:

"Sooner or later people will have to learn to live in a way my ancestors did, in a way that does not use up the irreplaceable resources of the country."

This statement, coming from a man close to nature, has the force of prophecy. Solar energy will supplant conventional sources first in remote places, where fuel is scarce or expensive because of transportation costs. India is such a place, as are regions of Mexico, ripe for solar devices to take the place of wood and animal power.

Providentially there is ample sunshine in many of these depressed lands. Here solar stoves and pumps, as well as other machines, will first have practical use. But slowly such devices will find their way back to more civilized countries as other fuel supplies begin to disappear.

At the time Edison invented the electric light no one accurately predicted the future of that glowing bulb. Neither was the fantastic radio and television industry foretold when De Forest gave the world the audion tube in 1907. Similarly it is impossible to say just what life will be like a hundred years from now, but we can make some fairly "educated" guesses. The picture we see is fascinating.

It is the year 2,050. We are living in the United States, population over 400 million. Surprisingly, cities are no larger than they were in 1950, although many of these large cities are now in the southwest. Most people live in smaller communities, spread over a wider area than in the past. It is in such a place, a town we will call Solarville, that we find ourselves. Let's spend a typical day there.

The electric alarm wakes us, and as we dress we notice the sun is just peeking over the horizon to the east. It is midwinter, and the temperature outside is a chilly 35 degrees. The house is comfortably warm, though, and we hear the faint movement of air through the wall registers. The air conditioner stores heat chemically, and even two consecutive cloudy days last week were no bother.

Lights come on in the bathroom at the flick of a switch

and the electric razor hums busily. Glancing out the window we look across the ten-foot stretch of water, seeing trees and other houses similar to ours, but no power poles or unsightly wires.

Atop our house, serving the double function of roof and power supply, is the slanted collector area. Its angle was carefully planned to be most effective, and the house itself floats in the circular pool of water, turning slowly during the day to follow the sun.

This is a much nicer home than the one we moved from last year. The old house was built on solid ground, with a stationary collector so that there were times when the storage batteries ran dangerously low and we had to use power sparingly. This new model is one of the finest available and we are very proud of it as we go into the kitchen for breakfast.

Bacon and eggs smell delicious cooking on the electric range, and the toast is kept warm in the solar oven alongside. As we sit down we listen to the radio describing plans for the first space trip to the planet Mercury. It will not be a simple trip like the scheduled runs to Mars or Venus, and the space ship is powered by the newest solar drive.

As we get up we cast a shadow across the radio and its volume fades until we pass. Smiling, we think about the kidding we take for being attached to the ancient portable that grandfather gave us so many years ago, but it still plays well. Of course the table model radio and the television set are plugged into the house current and are not subject to fading.

The house has turned a little since we got up, but we are used to that by now and it would seem odd if it didn't. Actually it makes for more variety in the view out the circular, insulated-glass walls. Returning a pitcher of juice to the refrigerator, we carry dishes to the sink and stack them in the dishwasher.

The washing machine and dryer are in the kitchen too, using power and hot water supplied with solar energy. The water is sterilized of course, since we pump our own out here in the suburbs. As we slip on a jacket, the air conditioner goes off. With the sun up now, enough heat is coming in through the glass walls to warm the house nicely. The roof will store heat for reserve, and then make power for a good part of the day.

Stepping out into the brisk morning air we circle the house until we reach the access walk. As we go across, the water in the pool doesn't look as inviting as it did in the summer, although if we did want to swim in winter we could warm the water quite easily. Besides its function as pool and turntable for the house, the water serves as heat storage tank and as part of the summer air conditioning cycle.

Passing through the low hedge surrounding the pool, we walk to the garage to get the car. Our garage is stationary, its fixed collector roof providing ample power to recharge the car's batteries, and for the little hobby work we do with power tools. Some friends with several cars and a big shop have automatic tracking collectors even on their garages, however.

Behind the garage the solar pump is busy, and we remember to go wind the clockwork motor that will turn its collector several times during the day. When we first moved away from city-provided water we had some doubts about maintaining a pump and the other hardships of country living, but now we smile when we remember. The

Association For Applied Solar Energy

SOMETIME IN THE future suburban homes may look like this. Floating in a pool of water, the entire glass-walled structure rotates so that the collector mounted on top of the roof always faces the sun. Power for lighting and appliances, as well as complete air conditioning, is provided by the sun. The pool serves for swimming and also heat storage during the winter.

saving on utilities is more than enough to make up for the cost of the car we commute with.

Lifting the garage door, we go inside. There is a faint hum from the battery charger and that reminds us to check the condition of the batteries in the car. The needle shows what should be enough power remaining for the trip to work, but to be on the safe side we lift the hood. It takes only a few minutes to lift out the batteries and replace them with freshly charged ones from the rack. Grumbling at this slight inconvenience, we promise to have the alignment of the car's wheels checked.

It is a two mile ride to the business district where we work and the trip takes only a few minutes. The car is small and light in weight, made principally from magnesium. This metal is now one of the cheapest, being a by-product of the huge distilling plants that produce fresh water along the coast.

The traffic lane on the outside is used by interurban buses, electrically-driven and taking their power from the collector strip alongside the highway. This same source, municipally maintained, provides electricity for street and traffic lights as well as emergency charging facilities for motorists.

As we pass the airfield, a transport plane takes off and heads east towards the sun. Powerful rocket motors, fueled with liquid oxygen, or "lox" as it is called, remind us of our job at the fuel plant. With a degree in solar technology, we found a position as engineer with Allied Decomp, where sea water, piped five hundred miles from the Gulf, is broken down into the gases of oxygen and hydrogen.

Since fuel can be made nearly anywhere now, its transportation is a thing of the past. Thus sea water flows

Association For Applied Solar Energy

THIS POWER STATION, built on the outskirts of a city of tomorrow, uses solar energy to convert water into the gases, hydrogen and oxygen. The gases are then burned as fuel, or allowed to recombine in what are called "Bacon cells" which produce electricity. If the city lies on the coast, it may use sea water, converting a part of it to fresh water for drinking, and using the salt by-product that is formed.

through the pipes that once carried fuel oil and natural gas. Each city of any size makes its own gas fuels, along with numerous by-products. Airplanes require this type of power and some heating is done by gas during prolonged bad weather. Then too, hospitals and many industries use oxygen and hydrogen. Our job with Allied is an important one and we are proud of the work we do.

Parking under the long, shed-like shelter, we pause long enough to attach charging wires to the car's batteries. The shelter is also a solar collector and furnishes electricity for all the cars parked under it. By the time we come from the plant when the shift is over the batteries will be completely recharged. Some places charge for this convenience, but Allied offers it free to employees.

The day goes well, except for some valve trouble in the west wing of the tank building. By noon we have located the cause, re-routed the flow of liquid and made a replacement of the corroded part. The salt content of the water is near the safe maximum and we make a report to that effect. Then we go to lunch.

Our meal is excellent, the meat and fresh vegetables matched ounce for ounce with algae supplement. *Chlorella* processers are so skillful now that it is hard to tell where the cooks have used the various powders, gelatins and liquids. Times have changed a lot from when the government first announced that land farms could no longer feed the country! In those early days *chlorella* all seemed to have a fishy odor in spite of what a cook could do to doctor it.

The afternoon passes quickly, and as the air outside cools, blowers route surplus warmth from the sunny side of the plant to the shaded side. Once it would have seemed

Association For Applied Solar Energy

FOR INLAND CITIES where surplus water is not available, a different kind of solar power plant may come into use. Inexpensive flat plate collectors of ordinary glass trap the sun's heat in this picture. A steam-generating station provides electricity. Notice the power lines leading into the distance.

odd to have to cool a building and warm it at the same time, but this has been standard practice for some time.

Before leaving the plant, we stop at the fountain for a drink of cold water. Water is no longer the distressing problem in the southwest it was a hundred years ago and it is hard to believe people once were driven out of dry parts of the country! Today sea water is piped hundreds of miles to make the desert literally bloom again. Instead of dropping as it did for so long, the water table is rising so that outlying areas now pump their own water as we do for our house.

Back at the car we notice that the charging cables have automatically disconnected and reeled up into the overhead. The needle on the instrument panel tells us the batteries are fully charged so we drive away from the parking shed. There are quite a few cars on the road but we compare it with stories read of the old days when everyone worked in a huge city. The thought makes us smile sympathetically. Solar living has brought many bonuses.

By the time we shop a bit and then return home, the sun is fairly low in the west and the air is chilly. Shivering slightly we put the car in the garage, duck around back to check the pump, and then hurry for the house. It has turned almost completely around from the way it was in the morning, the gleaming collector on the roof catching the last rays from the sun.

We cross the access walk and the kitchen door is right in front of us. Inside, the air is warm and the drawn drapes create a cozy effect. The smell of dinner cooking wrinkles our noses with pleasure, and we hear the voice of a newscaster on television. We glance at the screen and see a picture of the new space ship, almost ready to leave on its

Association For Applied Solar Energy

SOLAR ENERGY can convert salt water, or water otherwise undrinkable, into fresh water and make areas once useless available for raising stock. It would also be possible to grow algae by the open pond method and use it for feed.

epoch-making journey to Mercury. Wistfully we think that this is the threshold of a new era and wonder what it will be like a hundred years from now!

Our day in Solarville was fanciful, of course. What life will be like in 2,050 we cannot say for sure, but the things we have described are all based on known fact. When the Wright brothers first flew, not even the wildest fanatic would have dared predict things we now take as commonplace—jet airliners that travel five hundred miles an hour, and experimental planes capable of three times that speed.

The steam engine and other inventions once caused a revolution in our lives, and kept the dire predictions of Malthus from becoming grim facts. Solar energy may not revolutionize things, but it will change them. We will live to see some of those changes; one day other people may live *because* of those changes.

621.47   Halacy, D.
.H157F   Fabulous fireball: the
         story of solar energy.